BE'ER HAGOLAH INSTITUTES
671 LOUISIANA AVENUE
BROOKLYN, NEW YORK 11239

I did not come to this country to save myself or to seek positions of personal power," Rabbi Kotler said. *"Rather, I am here so that, with your help, we can save our brothers and the centers of Torah learning all over Europe!"*

"On the other side of the ocean our brothers are waiting for our help," he continued. *"Only you, the Jews of America, are able to help them. Do it now! Save them!"*

Rabbi Aharon Kotler

In our generation, thousands of Russian children are landing on American shores each year. And it is now up to us to make the sacrifices.

Be'er Hagolah Institutes was founded over a decade ago to combat the forces that were preventing the ideals of Judiasm from reaching the *neshamos* of these innocent children.

There are presently over 1000 students studying at our school. This number is increasing dramatically each year as a result of the tremendous influx of new Soviet immigrants. Be'er Hagolah's outstanding staff of teachers, guidance counselors, family educators, and professionals offer a full range of educational programs for the students and their parents, as well as social experiences such as family *shabbatonim, chavrusa* programs with *bnei yeshivah,* Big Sister-Little Sister, Bais Yaakov programs, summer camping and countless other activities; all geared to introduce and inspire them to Torah living.

"Each generation must answer to a different test. Our generation will have to give testimony regarding what we did for Russian Jews."
Harav Hagaon R'Yaakov Kaminetsky *zt"l*

Meet the Children
of
Be'er Hagolah!

Nisson Safiev
compesition

Dec. 20, 1991
Miss Engel

What Be,er Hagolah
did for me!

My name is Nisson Safiev. I am 10 years old. I go to Be,er Hagolah. If it wasn't for Be,er Hagolah I would be going to public school because my mother couldn't pay so much money. So I came to Be,er Hagolah. And I have 'Leared alot.'.

One שבת I thought I wanted to do a Big מצוה, so I was thinking it's שבת today. My mother dosn't keep שבת but, I try very hard to keep שבת because it is a very big מצוה. So me and my little sister went in the kichen and I took a look at the time I said to my sister go dress up for שבת. I lit the candles and me and my sister said the ברכה. And that's how I got to know what שבת is all About. I Love שבת

Fina Kriechmar
Grade 5

Compasion

<u>A Shabbos in Russia</u>

A Shabbos in Russia isn't good
because they don't let no jews do Shabbos
and when its war time they kill the jews
just because there jewish lots of my
grandfather brothers and sisters were killed
because there jewish and espesialy if they have
anything like a Siddar they rip it up and
doesn't let them davven that's why its not
good to do Shabbos in Russia and
if you don't davven by perpus then you get a
ברכה but if ה' knows that you want to
davven but the soldiers don't let so ה' makes
the soldier bad luck.

But in america yo could be relegios you
I know that everybody
like to do Shabbos
My parents don't know
from school I learn
parents how to do ar
they like it.

שבת

In Russia it was hard to keep Shabbos
for those who knew what it is. It
was harder for us kids, because on suturday
we were suppose to go to school, and
write and carry brifcases, and to get
home we had to ride on buses and cars.
But now my family and I came to America.
I went to Yeshiva and every thing about Shabbos and
me enin and every thing about Shabbos and
every holliday there is. Teachers in our
school, thought that it would be a great
idea to take the school on the Shabbaton.
On shabbotons we had a lot of fun,
and we did learn a lot about Shabbos.
The people that we went for Shabbos
taught us Brachos, and some of the דינים
like keeping Kosher, keeping shabbos, and
צניעות. They taught us why we have
to wear long skirts and sleeves. They
also taught us why we can't turn on the
light on Shabbos or cook. They explaned
why we can't work on Shabbos. They said
that ה' created the world on six days,
and on the seventh day he rested,''
that is why we rest on Shabbos.

By. דבורה Vilkov.

Dear Principal, Teachers, and Staff of
Be'er Hagolah,

It's hard to express my feelings on a dead piece of paper that I had when I saw a book about Chanukah in Russian in the hands of my granddaughter, Victoria.

I am Victoria's grandmother. I was born in a Jewish religious family, but at the age of fourteen I had to depart from them.

While I was living among the Russians and was surrounded by people that were hostile to Jews, I couldn't keep the Laws of my religion. I also couldn't give my daughter a Jewish education because I didn't know very much to teach her and besides there are no Jewish schools in the USSR at all, but nevertheless, I taught her all the laws which I remembered and I tried to find out the dates of the Jewish holidays. I always considered as the most important holiday. For this reason I always fasted on that day and I still do. I felt that by fasting on G-d will forgive me for my ignorance of the religion and for my sins.

Now that we are in America in such a wonderful and free country, we want to take advantage of the freedom and I want Victoria to know the language, history of the Jewish people, and everything that we didn't have a chance to learn.

Since the age of fourteen I had to work very hard. In 1943 my husband came back as an invalid from the war. My parents were killed by Hitler in 1942, Let our children and grandchildren not know what we went through. Amen!

Thank you very much for your care and work. I wish you all happiness and health.

TAMARA KOTSAT

more letters at back of book

FAIGIE NEWMAN

If Only

C·I·S

P·U·B·L·I·S·H·E·R·S

New York · London · Jerusalem

For Dovid

Published and distributed
in the U.S., Canada and overseas by
C.I.S. Publishers and Distributors
180 Park Avenue, Lakewood, New Jersey 08701
(908) 905-3000 Fax: (908) 367-6666

Distributed in Israel by
C.I.S. International (Israel)
Rechov Mishkalov 18
Har Nof, Jerusalem
Tel: 02-518-935

Distributed in the U.K. and Europe by
C.I.S. International (U.K.)
89 Craven Park Road
London N15 6AH, England
Tel: 81-809-3723

Book and cover design: Deenee Cohen
Typography: Nechamie Miller and Chaya Bleier
Cover illustration: Maureen Scullin

ISBN 1-56062-194-X hard cover
1-56062-195-8 soft cover
Library of Congress Catalog Card Number
93-070341

PRINTED IN THE UNITED STATES OF AMERICA

ACKNOWLEDGMENTS

It is with great thanks to *Hakadosh Baruch Hu* that I have completed the writing of this book. Along the way I have been fortunate to have had the help and encouragement of many friends. In particular, I would like to mention the following people:

Mrs. Miriam Elias for always being just a phone call away. Her insightful suggestions and down-to-earth guidance is only surpassed by her wonderful personality and natural warmth.

Rebbitzen Perlow, who, by giving generously of her time and sharing her wisdom and experience with me, helped form the characters of this book.

Rebbitzen Hoberman, who, since I have known her, has always said what should be said, whether I wanted it to be said or not.

Sara Stern, my summer neighbor and winter friend. A co-conspirator and pen pal who truly empathized with me over each word, sentence, paragraph, etc.

9

Tzippy Braude for her kind help.

Mrs. Sara Braunstein for her cheery prognosis.

Dr. David Spiegel and Dr. Moshe Hecht for answering all my medical questions.

My brother-in-law Dr. Moshe Akerman, who stayed up to the wee hours of the night to explain every medical contingency and possibility that exists.

Channie and Moshe, Rachel and Shlomo, Hadassah and Elazar, Michel and Channie, Eliezer and Chana Etka, Nava and Hillel for their encouragement.

My dear parents, Rabbi and Mrs. Gurkov, for all they have done and continue to do for me.

My other parents, Mr. and Mrs. Newman, whose warmth and love have been appreciated since day one.

Raizy Kaufman and Rabbi Reinman at C.I.S. Publishers for all their help and advice.

Miriam Adahan, who graciously gave me permission to incorporate some of her E.M.E.T.T. tools into this book.

My wonderful children, Yehuda, Eli, Estie, Tzvi, Miriam and Leah, just for being who they are.

Most of all, I thank my husband Dovid. His constant encouragement, good advice and devotion have helped me tremendously, not only in every aspect of writing this book, but in our life together, each and every day.

1

Shevy woke up to a cold dark night. She slowly propped herself up on her pillows and pulled the comforter snugly around her neck and shoulders. The noises coming from the adjoining room were the kind that twelve-year-old Shevy was used to by now. Through the thin walls, Shevy could hear her mother's muffled crying and the sliding of the closet door. She could hear her father's footsteps as he went out to the hall bathroom. More noise. The water running, the medicine cabinet slamming shut.

Back in the bedroom, Shevy's father handed her mother a pill. "Here, Nechami, take this," he said consolingly as he closed the door. "You'll feel better."

He continued talking, his tone gentle and reassuring. With the door closed, Shevy couldn't hear what he said. But eventually her mother's sobbing subsided, and she too began to speak softly, her tones laced with fear.

Shevy sighed. Slowly, unbidden tears coursed down

her cheeks. She tasted the salty liquid with the tip of her tongue. I'm so scared, she thought for the hundredth time that week. Please, Hashem, I'm so scared!

"Tova," she called quietly to her sister in the bed across from her. "Tova, wake up."

"Huh?" came a tired, muffled response. "What is it? What time is it?"

"I don't know. Tova, I'm too scared to sleep!"

"Oh." Tova turned over, now completely awake and aware. "Please, Shev, don't think so much. Go back to sleep. It'll be morning soon, and you'll feel better then." Tova turned back over and put her head on the pillow.

"Tova, please come into my bed. I'm so scared."

Wordlessly, Tova climbed out of her own bed and into Shevy's. "Good night," she said and promptly fell asleep.

Lying back on her pillow, Shevy tried to sleep, tried not to think, but in the still of the night, her thoughts were all she had. It was only five months since they had found out that their mother was sick. Cancer. The doctor had told them that the chances of her being cured were great, and that they were lucky for finding out about it so soon. Lucky. Yeah. Real lucky.

Another tear coursed down Shevy's cheek. Determinedly, she tried to clear her mind and fall asleep, but it was only when the first faint misty morning light trickled in through the bedroom window that Shevy managed to drift off.

Morning. In the morning Shevy always felt better. She was able to put her fears aside, at least for a little while. The nagging anxiety was a creature of the night. It waited patiently, quietly, for the Quiet Times. The Thinking Times. Then it came creeping out and began to tug at her heart.

Oh! Look at the time! Shevy exploded out of her bed, throwing off the last traces of her melancholy mood together with her pajamas. She washed her hands with the speed of lightning. Her hands worked swiftly, automatically choosing her clothing and she was dressed in no time. Her mind was already downstairs, mentally going through her briefcase to make sure that she had everything she needed for school.

Snap!

Shevy stared down at the broken shoelace clutched in her fingers and groaned. She was already late for school, and now this! Why did shoelaces always break when you were in the biggest rush?

Expertly, Shevy kicked her shoes off her feet and into the air. They spun like little pinwheels, curving across the room in graceful arcs and landing neatly in the closet. Shevy wasn't watching them, though. She was already rummaging under the bed for another pair.

Shevy hurtled out of her room toward the stairs, but as she passed her mother's room, she came to a screeching halt. She hesitated for a moment, took a deep breath and knocked at her mother's door softly.

"Come in," said her mother in her soft and gentle way.

Shevy looked around the dim bedroom. Her eyes traveled over the night table, which was covered, as usual, with brown plastic pill boxes and came to a rest on her mother's prone figure. Her mother's normally slight build seemed even smaller, her body almost lost in the covers. Her face, usually bright with expression, seemed lined and weary.

"Good morning, Imma," said Shevy. "How do you feel?"

"*Baruch Hashem*. Every day is better."

"How was your night, Imma?" Shevy asked, knowing what her mother would answer.

"Fine, sweetheart. Thank you for asking. Have a good day at school, and please, this time, eat some breakfast before you go!"

"Okay, Imma. Feel good."

Shevy bent down to kiss her mother and started to leave. She stopped at the door and quickly turned around. "I love you, Imma."

Downstairs, Shevy found her father eating breakfast with her two younger brothers in the family's large yellow kitchen.

Shevy looked up at her father. He was a tall, handsome man with brown, expressive eyes behind large, thick eyeglasses. A short black beard framed his face, with gray hairs prominent at his temples. Shevy remembered Imma's claim that before they were married, Abba had been as thin as a toothpick. Abba always added that Imma's cooking was so good that he couldn't help gaining an extra pound or two.

"Good morning!" he greeted her cheerfully.

"Hi!" Shevy snatched a banana and a yogurt from the kitchen table and started out the kitchen door, her long brown hair flying behind her. "Bye!"

"Hold it! Why don't you sit down and eat? What's the rush?"

"I'm late to school. I'm sorry I can't help you with breakfast. Bye!"

"Bye! But you might regret this hasty departure at noontime today," said her father solemnly as he peered down over his glasses, one hand behind his back.

"What?" Shevy looked up at him quizzically. "Why?"

"Lunch."

With a theatrical flourish, he pulled his hand from behind his back and lifted it in the air. Shevy's lunch bag was in his hand. Shevy's brothers giggled.

"Have a fulfilling day," her father joked.

Shevy and ten-year-old Motty groaned at the pun. After she retrieved her lunch from her father's outstretched hand, Shevy continued out the door.

"Oh, I get it," said Yehudah, a first-grader. "Full-filling!"

Shevy ran all the way to the bus stop, lunch in one hand, books in the other. When she got there, breathless and flustered, all she saw was the back end of the bus half a block away, already merged with traffic.

Late again, thought Shevy. The second time this week. Mrs. Krigsman is going to be real upset.

For a desperate moment, Shevy considered chasing the bus, but she was simply too tired to try. She hopped from foot to foot in the chilly, post-*Sukkos* air, twirling her hair behind her and pulling on her hood.

It was another ten minutes until the next bus came, and Shevy was grateful for the burst of warm, fan-forced air that hit her in the face as she boarded the bus. She sat back in her seat and savored the delicious warmth, closing her eyes and feeling the relaxing vibration of the bus's rumbling motion. She smiled to herself dreamily, feeling the tension drain out of her tired body. Shevy exhaled a long sigh of relief.

Her good mood did not last long. It was a Quiet Time, and the creature emerged from its lair and gripped her mind. Her mother's illness once again filled her thoughts, and she began to remember . . .

It was right before the summer that Shevy's mother, Nechami Feder, had started feeling very tired and weak. She tried resting, but continued to feel worse and worse and finally went to the doctor. She came back from Dr. Shanowitz very upset and went straight to the bedroom. Shevy's father came home from work earlier than usual and called all the kids together.

That night was forever stamped in Shevy's memory. For the first time in her life, Shevy had seen her father frightened.

"The doctors aren't sure what it is that's wrong," he said, his eyes wandering off to the side. "Imma will be going to the hospital tomorrow afternoon for a few days of testing. We'll tell you any results as soon as we know them. Right now, we have to make sleeping arrangements for you for the rest of the week."

A week? Was Imma so sick that it would take a week just to find out what was wrong with her?

Shevy had ended up spending the week at her friend Rivkah's house. It was a little strange. At any other time, it would have been a blast to spend a week at her best friend's house. But now, Shevy was a nervous wreck. She kept wondering what was happening with her mother.

Although her parents called her each night, they didn't really tell her what was going on. In school, her mind constantly wandered off, and when she went to Rivkah's house after school, she was in no mood for fun.

Towards the end of that week, Shevy and Tova had gone to the hospital to visit. Imma put on a cheerful front, but the girls could tell that it was forced. She kept looking away from them, out the window, staring at nothing. Finally, she just started crying. Abba nodded deliberately at Tante Elly, the girls' aunt, who promptly ushered them out of the room and into a small waiting room nearby.

"Your mother isn't really up to having any visitors, girls. It wasn't such a good idea for you to come here, anyway."

"What is it, Tante Elly?" asked Tova. "What's wrong with Imma?"

Tante Elly hesitated. She started to speak, but suddenly closed her mouth, as if unsure of how to proceed. Then she made up her mind.

"Hodgkin's disease," she said, gently but firmly.

Tova and Shevy said nothing. They didn't know what to say. They didn't even know what it meant. Shevy noticed, vividly, that the clock on the wall was making a kind of humming noise. Or maybe it was the fluorescent light.

Tante Elly continued to speak. "It's a kind of . . . cancer. But the doctors did lots of tests on her, and there is good news. The chances of your Imma getting better are very good. She'll have to come to the hospital every month for a few days to get treatments . . . something called chemotherapy. She'll probably feel weak and sick from it for a couple of days after she comes home, but in the end, it will make her better."

The chances of Imma getting better were good?

Chances?

Good?

Tante Elly continued talking, but Shevy could hardly listen. She felt very strange, sort of dizzy. She closed her eyes and gripped the coarse seat cushion tightly, waiting for the spinning in her head to stop. She couldn't even hear what Tante Elly was saying any more. Her voice was just a buzzing noise in the room, like the clock on the wall or the fluorescent light.

Just the thought of her mother *possibly* not getting better brought a terrible feeling to Shevy's insides. Her eyes flooded with tears. The salty water burst out of her and ran down her cheeks as if it would never stop. When Tova saw Shevy crying, she also started. Tante Elly made soothing noises and tried to calm them, but her face betrayed her own concern. Before long, she had started crying too.

Right before *Tishah b'Av*, Shevy's mother had begun her treatments. Every month since then, she had gone into the hospital for a few days at a time and had always returned home feeling incredibly weak and sick. The first two months were terrible. She had cried a lot, although she seemed to try not to. When Shevy came home from school, her mother would sound okay, but her eyes were puffy and red. At night, Shevy could always hear her crying.

Eventually, Mrs. Feder had stopped crying so often and seemed to accept what had happened. "Everything

Hashem does is for the best," she would say. But Shevy knew that her mother was scared.

Shevy was afraid too. She felt scared for her mother but also for herself. Worse, she was secretly ashamed that she was worried about herself when it was her mother who was so sick. She felt that something must be wrong with her. How could she be so selfish when her mother's life was in danger?

She wanted desperately to talk to Tova, to hear how Tova felt. Tova was two years older than Shevy and was in tenth grade. Shevy tried to talk with Tova about her feelings, but Tova seemed carefree and unconcerned about the whole situation.

"Tova," she asked hesitantly, "do you think Imma will get better soon?"

"Yeah, I guess so. Anyway, you want to help me with my science project?"

After a few similar attempts, Shevy gave up. She was amazed at her sister, who seemed to have forgotten about the entire matter. Instead of Tova, Shevy would go to her father or to her friend Rivkah for solace. When she wasn't talking to them, she was talking to herself. My mind these days, she thought bitterly, is just like the wheels of this bus. Round and round they go, endlessly, over and over again, always coming back to the same spot.

But the fear wasn't even the worst part of it. There was one thing that she never spoke about to anyone and never would. It was her deepest, most shameful secret. She had realized it right then and there in the horrible little hospital waiting room with Tante Elly, and it was that knowledge that had made her cry. The others thought that they knew why she was crying, but they were wrong. Only she knew the real reason, the awful truth.

Deep in her heart, Shevy knew that it was *her* fault that Imma was sick.

2

Opening the door and quietly entering Mrs. Krigsman's *Chumash* class, Shevy steeled herself for a stern interrogation. She was over twenty minutes late, and Mrs. Krigsman would not be pleased, to say the least. She ruled her class with an iron hand that none of the girls dared defy.

The classroom was totally silent. Shevy began to inch over to her seat. It was only a few feet, but the distance seemed to stretch for miles. She felt as if every pair of eyes in the class was on her. Of course, she was only really concerned about one particular pair of eyes.

"Shevy?" came the inevitable question, breaking the perfect silence of the classroom.

For a brief instant, Shevy thought about making up an excuse. But she realized that only the truth would do. "I'm sorry, Mrs. Krigsman. I missed the bus."

Shevy nervously waited for the well-dressed rebuke. After all, it was the second time this week that she was late. To her surprise, the rebuke never came.

"You may sit down," said Mrs. Krigsman mildly.

Gratefully, Shevy took her seat and opened her *Chumash*. After a few moments, she stole a glance around the room. She suddenly became aware that there was something different in the atmosphere today. The whole class seemed jumpy, excited and fidgety, hardly able to listen to Mrs. Krigsman, who usually commanded everyone's absolute concentration.

The only one in the class who appeared unaffected was Dinah, the brightest girl in the eighth grade. She was right up front, concentrating on every word of the lesson.

Shevy wondered what in the world was going on. Whatever it was, she was sure it was something big.

Shevy glanced over at Rivkah Akerman, her best friend, who was sitting beside her. Rivkah was looking right at Shevy, and as their eyes locked, Shevy saw the excited look in her friend's eyes. She shot Rivkah a questioning glance, but the exchange was stopped short when they saw Mrs. Krigsman staring sternly in their direction. Both girls turned back to their *Chumashim*.

After what seemed an eternity, class was finally over. Before the bell finished ringing, Rivkah yelled to Shevy, "Shevy! Shevy! You got it! You got it! You're in the play! And your part—you're *Evelyn*! It's the main part!" Rivkah grabbed Shevy's arm and squeezed.

"What? How do you know? Are you sure?" Shevy was so shocked she wasn't sure how to react.

"Mrs. Levy came in right before class started and posted the parts on the wall!"

"I'm your father, Shevy!" called Rachel excitedly from

the other side of the room.

"And I play your teacher, so watch it!" joked Ahuvah.

Shevy turned around to face Rivkah. Rivkah's short curly brown hair was bouncing, and her brown eyes were sparkling. Shevy thought back to kindergarten, when they first became friends after discovering, to their mutual delight, that they both enjoyed eating play-dough.

Rivkah was well liked in school. She had a warm personality mixed with a healthy measure of decisiveness and boldness. However, what was most endearing about Rivkah was that she befriended one and all. Shevy, a more serious and intense girl, who came to decisions only slowly and thoughtfully, was proud that Rivkah had chosen her as a best friend.

"Isn't this great! You've been looking forward to the play since third grade!" beamed Rivkah. Her tone seemed to indicate, *See, I knew everything would turn out okay! You worry for nothing!*

Rivkah took Shevy by the hand and led her to the bulletin board. "Look! See for yourself!"

Shevy looked at the paper tacked to the bulletin board, and sure enough, her name was on the cast list: "Evelyn—Shevy Feder"!

Shevy was thrilled. Her face lit up with a smile. The play! Shevy had wanted a part in the eighth grade play for as long as she could remember.

The annual eighth grade play was a major production and one of the highlights of the school year. The play was open to all women and girls, and the proceeds went to *tzeddakah*.

This year, the play was entitled *Evelyn in America*. It

was a comedy about a Jewish girl from Paris whose parents sent her to study at a famous secular high school in America. She mistakenly ends up in a *yeshivah*.

Shevy remembered back to the third grade, to the first time she had seen a play. It was, in fact, that year's eighth grade school play, and Shevy had been spellbound. The lights, the costumes, the music, the scenery, the story—it was all so magnificent and exciting!

Right then and there she had decided: I can do that, too! After that, the Feder family had been treated to dozens of *Shabbos* afternoon performances, until Shevy had outgrown that stage of her love of drama.

In summer camp, Shevy had gotten a chance to act on a real stage for a live audience. It had been a blast! Although her part wasn't too big or important, since all the main parts went to staff members or older campers, she had had the time of her life. She had helped out in any way she could, from collecting props and painting scenery to running off scripts on the camp's dilapidated ditto machine.

"Rivkah! It's true! I got it! I really got it!"

"Of course it's true, silly," replied Rivkah.

Shevy turned to face her friend. "Rivkah! I was so excited that I forgot to ask if you got what you wanted. Are you part of the dance?"

"I am! I don't like acting like you do, but I love dancing." With that, Rivkah did a dramatic pirouette and curtsied gracefully.

Shevy gave Rivkah a standing ovation. The two best friends collapsed into their seats and joined the rest of the class in joyfully discussing the upcoming production.

Only Dinah seemed oblivious to the raucous hullaba-
loo. She was sitting hunched over her looseleaf, wearing
an intense frown of concentration as she painstakingly
finished her notes.

3

Shevy burst into the house and dropped her school bag on the front hallway floor.

"Imma, Imma!" she called breathlessly, running down the long hallway and into the kitchen.

"Guess what! Oh, Tova—hi! Where's Imma?" Shevy was gushing excitement from every pore in her body.

Tova looked up from preparing supper, her eyes wide with curiosity. "In the living room lying down. She's not feeling too well. But what's so exciting? Did you get it? Did you get a part?"

"Yes! Yes! Yes! I got a part! A big part! I can't believe it! I really did! I'm so excited!"

"Shevy! That's great! When is it? What's the play about? Can I read the script?" asked Tova, instantly caught up in the excitement.

"I'll tell you soon. I just want to tell Imma first, and then I'll tell you everything."

Shevy ran into the living room. Her mother was lying

on the couch reading a book, and Yehudah was nearby playing with his Etch-a-Sketch.

"Imma! I got a part! I'm Evelyn!"

"Shevy, that's absolutely fantastic," said Imma, sitting up. "I know how much you wanted it. Your face is beaming with joy! I haven't seen you so happy since . . . since . . . well, for a long time!"

Shevy pulled a rolled up wad of paper out of her pocket. "Look, here's the script. If you'd like, you can read it."

"Shevy, I'd love to read it!"

Motty and Tova came into the room. "Tova told me you got a part in the play. Is it a big one?" asked Motty.

"Yup! The biggest!" Everyone crowded around the couch as Shevy told them the story of the play.

When she was done, Motty shook his head in amazement. "This play sounds great! It has everything—jokes, scary parts, Jewish stuff. Can I come see it?"

"Yeah! Me, too," piped up Yehudah. "I want to come also. I'll sit right next to Imma. I'll even take pictures. Maybe Sruly will come with us and . . ."

Mrs. Feder burst out laughing. When Yehudah started talking, he could go on and on.

"Well, boys don't come to the production at all, Yehudah. But if you want, I can use your help with my costume," said Shevy.

"Oh," said Yehudah disappointedly. Then his face brightened as a thought occurred to him. "Hey, can Imma go?"

"Of course Imma can come! All the mothers are going to be there, just like every year . . ."

Shevy stopped short as she was struck with a thought. "Oh, Imma, *can* you come? Will you be home then or in the hospital?"

It seemed that Shevy's mother hadn't thought of the hospital either, because when she looked up, her face was pale. "Well," she said thoughtfully, "this is too exciting and important to miss. I'll arrange the dates so that I don't have to be in the hospital then. Tova, please get my calendar from the kitchen."

Tova soon returned, and Mrs. Feder leafed through the calendar. When she looked up, she was smiling with relief.

"No problem!"

Tova took the calendar back to the kitchen, calling over her shoulder, "I have to get back to supper, Shev, but the play sounds terrific!"

"Even if I had been scheduled to go into the hospital then, I'd have changed the dates, Shevy," Mrs. Feder said.

"Oh, Imma, thanks so much! As much as I'm thrilled about this, it just wouldn't be the same without you there to see it!" She gave her mother an impulsive kiss on the cheek.

Mrs. Feder laughed and kissed her in return. "Go in the kitchen and eat, sweetie. I'm a little tired. I'm going to take a nap."

"Okay, Imma. But when is Abba coming home? I can't wait to tell him!"

"He'll be home in around an hour for a quick supper. He has to go back to the office later to make up some time. After that, he's going to Mr. Jacobs' house to learn and won't be home until late. I suppose you'll have to catch him before he leaves."

Shevy watched as her mother pulled the worn afghan snugly around her shoulders and sank back onto the couch. Yehudah was still glued to his seat, only inches away from his mother, once again involved in his toy.

Quietly, Shevy sat and watched her sleeping mother. Her chest made small, ragged rising and falling motions. Shevy looked intently at her mother and remembered. With shock and sorrow, she realized that in her excitement over the play she had forgotten all about her mother's illness.

She must be feeling horrible, Shevy thought sadly. I didn't even ask how she was feeling. All I care about is myself and my part in the play! Instead of worrying about important things, I'm only concerned about having fun.

Shevy shook her head as if waking up from a dream. With a determined expression, she made her way into the kitchen.

"Tova, let me help you with those potatoes."

"It's okay, Shevy. I'm almost finished. And you have cleanup tonight, anyway. After supper, I'm going to Naadia's house to study. Besides, it's my turn to cook tonight. Why do you want to do it?" Tova put down the peeler and watched Shevy, waiting for an answer.

"I just do, that's all."

"Well, I must say, that's strange. You never used to want to take over my jobs."

"I never used to do a lot of things," said Shevy quietly.

"Whatever that means. Look, since Imma got sick, you get into these weird moods. It's like you're suddenly an angel or something, and it really bugs me! In any case, I don't need your help!" Tova ended in almost a shout.

"Why are you yelling?"

"I'm not yelling!" yelled Tova, gesturing dramatically with her peeler. "Just bug off, and stop making a big deal over everything."

"I'm not. All I asked is if you wanted me to peel potatoes, and you got all nutty! You never used to be like this, you know!"

"Why don't you just go and find someone else to do your good deeds for?" screamed Tova, her face reddening in anger.

Shevy was only too happy to get away from Tova. It's funny, she thought. Everyone always comments on how Tova and I must have been cast from the same mold. The same long, silky brown hair and eyes, the same tall, graceful figure, even the same laugh. Yet for all the physical similarities, our temperaments and thoughts are sometimes a long, long way apart. Especially these days, thought Shevy.

Later that night, Shevy and her father were in the kitchen happily discussing Shevy's costume for the play. Mr. Feder was a graphic artist by trade and exceptionally creative by nature. He was always in charge of designing and creating the Purim and play costumes for the Feder household.

Shevy and her father sat together at the long kitchen table while he finished his supper and Shevy peeled an orange. The clock ticked quietly above them as they went over the final details of the costume.

"So, my leetle croissant," said Mr. Feder in a fake

French accent, "by zee time you are feenished, you will luk more French zen zee French zemselves. And now, please to pass me zee French Fries. I haf to leave soon, my French Toast."

"Oh, Abba!" laughed Shevy, passing the plate across the table. "Thanks for all your help!"

"It's a small price to pay to see my daughter so happy!"

Motty walked into the kitchen and went to the refrigerator.

"Motty, any homework tonight?" asked Abba.

"I guess so. I'll get to it soon."

"You do that. I'd rather not have any more notes from your *Rebbi,* if you know what I mean."

Motty gave a guilty look and nodded his head. He was saved from further discussion by the ringing phone. He answered it and handed the phone to Shevy. Shevy took the phone and heard Rivkah's excited voice.

"Shevy, hi. Did you tell your parents about the part? Did you look at the script? There's dance practice during lunch tomorrow. I can't wait!"

"Rivkah," laughed Shevy, "I think you sound more excited about my part than I am."

"I am excited! But what I'm really calling you about is tonight. Ahuvah invited you and me to come to her house. Her parents bought her 8-Down for her birthday."

8-Down was the newest game on the market, and everyone age ten and above wanted it.

"She also has almond crunch ice cream. Sounds great, huh? My father will be over in five minutes to pick you up, okay?" asked Rivkah.

"She really has 8-Down? And ice cream? I'd love to

come! . . . No. Wait a minute. My sister is leaving soon, and so is my father. My mother just came home from the hospital a few days ago, and she isn't feeling so great. I don't think I should go."

"Shevy," interrupted Mr. Feder. "Go ahead. There's no reason for you to stay here."

Shevy just waved her hand and shook her head. "It's okay, Rivkah," she said into the telephone. "You go. I'll see you at school tomorrow. Bye."

"Well, it won't be the same without you. Are you sure?"

"Yes. Really. I'll see you tomorrow."

Shevy hung up the phone and looked up to see her father regarding her quizzically.

"Why didn't you go? Imma can take care of herself, and I know she'd be happy if you would go."

"No, Abba, I don't mind staying home."

Mr. Feder got up from the table and brought his dishes to the sink. "I don't know, Shev. I don't like it. I don't have time to talk to you right now, but I'll see you later. Have a good night," he said, giving Shevy a kiss.

"Good night, Abba. I'll see you tomorrow. And I'll give the boys breakfast in the morning."

"Hmm . . ." was Mr. Feder's only reply.

At school one week later, Shevy sat at her desk. The classroom was in the usual turmoil that preceded the morning bell. The atmosphere was boiling with motion and sound, as students continually streamed in and out of the room, taking off coats and frantically searching for books, papers and assignments. They produced a steady uproar of comments and conversation about everything and anything.

Shevy pulled out her well-worn pocket-sized calendar to cross off another day. Only two more weeks, and her mother would be in the hospital again. She also marked the day with a big letter P, as she had every day since the play parts were given out.

Shevy chewed on her pencil and thought about how fast the months seemed to fly by but how slowly each single day seemed to creep.

Looking up towards the front of the room, she saw Dinah, surrounded by a nervous group of unprepared students. Dinah graciously went through the homework many times until even the least advanced girl caught on. Everyone thanked her as if she had given them gold. It struck Shevy that instead of resenting having to spend every spare moment doing free tutoring, Dinah seemed to actually enjoy it.

Shevy took a moment to consider Dinah. She was of average height with light brown hair that just hit the nape of her neck. Round glasses magnified her large brown eyes and added to her studious appearance. Without question, Dinah had the highest average in the class and was the obvious candidate for future valedictorian. No one begrudged Dinah her abilities, since she more than willingly shared her knowledge with any girl who needed help.

Socially, however, Dinah didn't do nearly as well, thought Shevy. Only Shani was really friendly with her. But all things considered, she seemed comfortable enough in the class.

Shevy had no more time for her thoughts, as the door opened and Mrs. Krigman entered. Almost instantly, the girls were seated and quiet. This was not unusual, but what Mrs. Krigsman said next certainly was.

"*Boker tov*, girls. Before we start class, I'd like to introduce a new student. Her name is Shayna Leeba Weinberg, and she is sitting in the back row. I'm sure you'll all welcome her and make her feel at home."

Shevy turned around, and sure enough, there in the back row sat a new girl. Shevy figured that she must have been sitting there so quietly that no one had noticed her earlier. Shifting uncomfortably in her seat, her face a bright pink, Shayna Leeba gave a shy smile and nervously tugged on the end of a single long, dark brown braid that came down almost to her waist.

There was no more time for gawking, since Mrs. Krigsman quickly started class in her usual brusque and efficient manner. With her grade book open, she proceeded to quiz the girls on the previous day's lesson.

Question after question was answered correctly, mostly by Dinah. Finally, the teacher said, "Last question, girls, and it's a tough one. Where does the name of the month *Kislev* come from?"

Mrs. Krigsman scanned the room. Total silence. Right on cue, all heads swiveled towards Dinah. Dinah just sat there, red as a beet, her eyes scanning her notes frantically.

The entire class was shocked at this unusual occurrence. Even Mrs. Krigsman seemed a bit taken aback.

Shevy noticed a few girls turning their attention to the back of the room. She followed their gaze and was surprised to see the new girl tentatively raising her hand.

"Shayna Leeba?" asked Mrs. Krigsman, with an encouraging but slightly skeptical smile on her face.

"Umm . . ." began the wavering voice. "Actually, it's not a Jewish name. The name Kislev came from the Babylonians, the *Bavlim.*"

"Er . . . Excellent! That is one hundred percent correct, Shayna Leeba. I see you must have learned very well in your former school."

More total silence. The class didn't know how to react.

Shayna Leeba smiled weakly and looked down at her desk. She seemed to regret having opened her mouth, to prefer not to be the center of attention.

Shevy quickly looked at Dinah, who turned away almost immediately. But the look that Shevy had caught on Dinah's reddening face was a mixture of shock, shame, humiliation and defeat. Inexplicably, she felt her own face reddening, as if Dinah's embarrassment were her own.

Shevy wanted to whisper to Dinah to relax and not take it so seriously. However, it didn't seem like the right time to say anything to Dinah.

The school day continued, and when the last bell rang, Rivkah turned to Shevy.

"Let's go, Shev. I can't wait for supper. This new diet is really getting to me."

"Rivkah! I didn't know you were on a diet. How long have you been on it?"

Rivkah blushed. "Well actually, I just started this morning."

Shevy laughed and quickly gathered her books. The

two girls made their way outside and boarded the bus home.

"What do you think of that new girl Shayna Leeba? She seems kind of quiet."

"Yeah," agreed Rivkah. "But kind of smart, too! Did you see how she knew that answer in Mrs. K.'s class?"

"Yup. She also did pretty well in the rest of the classes. And I got the distinct impression that she was even holding back a lot of what she knew," observed Shevy.

Shevy thought for a moment. "You know, she dresses kind of different, with that long braid and those stockings she wears."

"She also has a different pronunciation of Hebrew," Rivkah mused. "Very different."

"Uh-huh."

"Well, it was only her first day. I'm sure we'll know more about her soon enough. And I guess we shouldn't be talking about her like this, anyway."

"Guess so. Besides, it must be really awful coming into a new school in the middle of the year."

"Yeah. Especially in the last year of school."

Shevy and Rivkah continued talking while holding on to the straps of the crowded bus. They made plans for *Chanukah*, which was coming up soon, and before they knew it, the bus had come to their stop.

"See you tomorrow," called Shevy as she went up her walkway. "Good luck on your, umm, diet!"

"Very funny, Shevy Feder! You can only laugh because you haven't dieted a day in your life!"

"Haven't needed to!" giggled Shevy in return. With a final wave to her friend, she pulled out her keys, unlocked the door and gently closed it behind her.

Shevy hung up her coat in the hall closet and set her books on the hutch. Walking down the hallway towards the kitchen, she heard her mother humming softly.

"Hi, Imma."

"Hi, Shev. Guess what? You and I are going out to the mall tonight."

"Really? Great!"

Earlier in the week, Shevy and her mother had made tentative plans to shop at the mall for material for Shevy's costume.

"Uh-huh! Right after supper."

"Oh! I still have bunches to study for the *Chumash* test." Shevy stood against the doorway thinking.

"Well, okay. I guess we'll just have to put it off till later," said Shevy's mother. "I hope we get another chance before I have to go back to the hospital," she added.

"No, no, let's go," said Shevy quickly. "I'll study afterwards. Besides, Rivkah and I studied last night."

Mrs. Feder was a bit skeptical, but she knew that Shevy was always a conscientious student, and she relented.

As soon as supper was over, Shevy and her mother put on their coats.

"Good-bye, children," said Mrs. Feder, her hand on the front doorknob.

"Bye, Imma," said Motty.

"Make sure you do your homework, Motty."

"Yeah, I know, I know! Homework, homework, home-work."

"Yehudah," Mrs. Feder said gently to her six-year-old

son, who was standing nearby wearing a worried expression. "We'll only be gone a short while. You go to sleep soon, okay?"

"Please, Imma, can I come with you? I'll be very good."

"No, I'm sorry, you can't."

Yehudah's beseeching smile vanished from his face, replaced with a pout.

"Where are you going, anyway?" asked Motty.

"Imma and I are going to the mall to get material for my costume."

"What do you need a costume for? Don't the French people wear regular clothing like we do here in America?"

"Well, Abba said he'd help me come up with something really authentic."

"What's authentic French?" asked Motty.

"You'll see when we get back. Let's go, Shevy," said her mother.

"Okay, Imma. Thanks, Tova, for doing supper cleanup tonight," added Shevy quickly.

"What thanks? We're just switching turns."

"Well . . . thanks anyway."

"It's no big deal. Why do you have to make such a big deal over everything?" asked Tova irritably.

"Why do you always have to get so upset over everything?" asked Shevy in return.

"Well," interjected Mrs. Feder brightly. "let's get going, Shevy, before all the stores close!"

"Ma . . . are you sure you're up to it?" asked Shevy.

"Yes!" Mrs. Feder answered emphatically. "Now let's go. You'd think we were going to the moon for a month with all these good-byes!"

"Yeah, Shevy. Just go already!" said Tova in an annoyed tone, her face set in a grimace.

At last, they left. As Mrs. Feder pulled the car away from the curb, Shevy turned to glance back at the house. She saw a small figure at the frosted front window. A face pressed against the glass, staring after them. It was Yehudah.

4

rs. Feder parked as close as she could to the mall, but she and Shevy still had a long walk across the large, freezing parking lot. As soon as they left the car, they were gripped from head to toe by the biting frosty air that shot right through their winter clothing. They ran, holding their coats tightly around them as the wind blew and whistled in their faces.

It had been three weeks since Mrs. Feder was last in the hospital, and she was feeling relatively well. She was happy to get out of the house and to have the opportunity to enjoy an outing with Shevy.

When the two of them finally entered the mall, they were laughing uncontrollably from their crazed race across the parking lot. The heated mall offered a welcome respite from the cold. Their faces were pink, and tiny, chilly tears dripped from the corners of their eyes. They were exhilarated by their run and stood huffing, puffing and smiling as they waited to catch their breath.

"Shevy, it's freezing outside," laughed Mrs. Feder.

"Brrr!" answered Shevy, looking at her mother's frozen face. "Are you okay?"

"Shevy! *Baruch Hashem*, I feel absolutely wonderful! You are not to worry this entire evening! We are here to buy you material and to have fun. Now let's go upstairs to "Sew There" and see what they have for us."

Mother and daughter enjoyed the walk through the mall. As they made their way along, their shoes clicked on the polished terrazzo tiles. Crowds of people were hustling and bustling in and out of the brightly lit stores. The smell of coffee and hot food wafted through the air. The atmosphere echoed with pleasant music, conversation, and the muted hum of heaters and escalators. There was a feeling of excitement in the air which added to the tingle of pleasure that Shevy and her mother got from being out for some special time together.

The pair rode up a long escalator together with the throngs of shoppers. Hesitating for a moment at the top to get their bearings, they turned right and entered a large sewing shop which boasted a wide assortment of sewing needs. There were many rows, each containing numerous bolts of material.

"Where should we start?" asked a bewildered Shevy.

"From the beginning. And we don't have to stop until we get to the very end," replied her mother whimsically.

A saleswoman approached them. She was very tall and bony and was wearing tortoise-shell glasses with little fake diamonds at the points. Her jet-black hair was pulled away from her face severely and done up in a tight bun.

"Can I help you?" she asked with a pinched smile,

removing her glasses and holding them in her hand.

"Thank you, but we're just looking," answered Mrs. Feder pleasantly.

"As you wish," she replied with the same tight smile, as she replaced her glasses, spun on her heels and walked away.

"Shevy! Look at this!" exclaimed Mrs. Feder as she spied a particular bolt. "This pink taffeta is beautiful. I think it would make a really elegant French dress."

"Oh, Imma! It is beautiful, but I don't think it's exactly right. Could we look around some more?"

"Of course!"

Shevy and her mother continued looking. First they considered a blue crinoline, then a smocked cotton, next a golden silk and finally a purple tulle. They looked at a pink organza, and then, in desperation, even contemplated a red gingham.

At last, one hour and fifty-three minutes later, they found themselves at the last bolt of the last row of material, without the slightest notion of what to buy. Bewildered, they looked at each other and then looked up. Standing in front of them was the same saleslady, wearing the same tight smile as before.

"So! Can I help you now?" she asked with a smug, self-satisfied air.

Mrs. Feder burst out laughing. "Thanks," she said, "but at this point, I think we're beyond help!"

"Very well. Good night." And with that, she stiffly walked away.

"Shevy," Mrs. Feder said, "our search is not over yet. There is one more store downstairs that carries material.

It's not as large, but we still might find something there that's just right!"

Downstairs, Shevy and her mother entered "Martha's Spinyard." Almost immediately, Shevy spotted a kelly-green moire that she knew would be perfect. Next to it was a moire in paisley, with the same shade of green as the predominant color. Shevy knew it would be ideal for the shawl that she had envisioned.

"Imma! Look! This would be perfect!"

"Yes, it would. And the price is excellent. Let's buy it right now. The store will be closing any minute."

Shevy and her mother made their purchase and left the store. Time had really flown by. All over the mall, shopkeepers were pulling down their gates and locking up.

"Shevy," said Mrs. Feder as she started the car and turned on the heater, "I had a wonderful time!"

"Imma, me too! Thank you so much!"

Mrs. Feder squeezed Shevy's hand tightly. "I love you so, Shevy."

She started driving but held on to Shevy's hand until they were well on their way home.

The next morning, Shevy woke up with a smile on her face. She nearly tripped as she ran over to look through the bag from "Martha's Spinyard." She opened it and fingered the beautiful cloth.

After dressing, Shevy gathered her books together, making sure that her *Chumash* notes were in order. Today was the day of the big test, and Shevy hoped she would do well. She felt a knot tighten in her stomach. She hadn't studied like she usually did, and she knew that the test would be hard. She was planning to get a few minutes of extra study time on the bus on the way to school.

Pushing away such disquieting thoughts, she went to the kitchen for some breakfast before heading to school.

"Hi, Shevy," said her father brightly as she entered the kitchen.

Expecting to find her mother in the kitchen, Shevy was taken by surprise. "Abba! What are you doing here?"

"What is that supposed to mean?" her father asked with an amused smile. "Aren't you happy to see your father?"

"Of course. Except that you're usually not here at this time unless Imma isn't feeling well. What happened? Where's Imma?"

"Shevy, it's no big deal. Imma was just feeling especially tired, so I told her to stay in bed and that I would take care of things. Yehudah and Motty have already left, and I'll be leaving in a minute too, so . . ."

"Oh!" interrupted Shevy with a cry. "I know why Imma is sick! She went to the mall last night! It was cold outside, and then we were there for hours!"

All the good feelings of the morning quickly vanished, as Shevy ran back toward the steps to check on her mother.

"Shevy!" called Mr. Feder. "Imma is sleeping now. Please don't worry so much. She just needs to rest a bit."

Shevy turned around and came back to the kitchen. She took a bowl from the drainboard, slapped it down on the kitchen table, filled it with cereal and milk and sat down at the table dejectedly.

"Shevy, have a good day and don't worry about Imma.

She's just tired! I have to leave now. See you later." Mr. Feder quickly put on his coat and left the house.

"Bye," said Shevy in a small voice, tears forming in her eyes.

"Okay girls, please stop writing," announced Mrs. Krigsman.

The thick, heavy silence in the room was broken by the click of nineteen pens dropping onto desks. The girls exhaled sighs of fatigue, slumping in their seats like deflated balloons.

"Please pass up the papers."

Shevy handed in her test worriedly. This was the single most important test of the marking period. Shevy had started studying a week before. But with play practice every day during lunch and once a week at night, Shevy's time was limited. To make matters worse, she had thrown caution to the wind last night and had gone on that excursion with her mother to the mall.

In addition, Shevy just couldn't seem to concentrate like she usually did. Even Rivkah had noticed. She had come to study with Shevy two nights before, attempting to cram all the learning into one session.

"Shevy," she had said, sitting on the floor with her back against Tova's bed, "what's wrong with you tonight? Usually when we study you don't let us do anything except . . . study! Now you seem like you're off in another world."

"What? Huh?" said Shevy, startled. "Never mind, Rivkah. Let's get going. We've hardly done a thing, and the test is in two days! It's already eight o'clock! That only leaves us two hours until your mother comes to pick you up!" she said, frantically leafing through her notebook.

"Well! That's better," laughed Rivkah, running her fingers through her short brown curls. "You're sounding more like your usual panicky self."

Rivkah took the pillow off Tova's bed, propped it behind her head and ran her toes luxuriously through the fluffy, pink carpeting as the two girls got down to some serious studying.

Now, in class, Rivkah stole a quick glance at Shevy. Shevy looked upset and worried. Only moments later, the bell rang, and Shevy ran over to Dinah.

"Dinah, what was the answer to that first Rashi question in the second section?"

"The answer was *eglah arufah*."

Shevy smacked her hand to her forehead and groaned. "I got it wrong! What about the first multiple choice at the end? Was it the *Cohen* or the *Levi*?"

"The *Cohen*," answered Dinah.

"Oh no, Dinah, I got it wrong!"

"Well, the test was very long, Shevy. Maybe you did okay on the rest of it."

"Those were the ones I thought I got *right*!"

Rivkah called from her desk, "Shevy, why are you so worried? We studied really well together. I think that I did okay."

Shevy stomped over to Rivkah. "Well, I don't think that I did okay. I think that I did really poorly. My mind was a blank! I don't think I've ever done this badly on a test in my life!"

"Oh well, you know Mrs. Krigsman," said Rivkah,

swinging her legs over the side of the desk to face Shevy. "She'll have the tests marked by tomorrow. No use worrying about it until then. Besides, I'm sure you did okay. You always do well in *Chumash*."

"You mean I used to do well in *Chumash*."

"Listen Shev, why worry when you could be happy instead?"

"Listen Rivkah, why be happy when you could be worried instead?" Shevy retorted stubbornly. She put her chin on her hand, slumped back in her chair, and mentally went over the test once more.

The rest of the day dragged on for Shevy. She spent the time worrying about her mother and the *Chumash* test. Then her thoughts turned to Rivkah. Why does Rivkah think everything is a joke? Nothing bothers her!

She thought about how sick her mother must be feeling back at home. My fault, Shevy brooded.

She thought about her brother Yehudah, who seemed to spend every moment he could glued to their mother, and about Motty, who seemed to spend every spare minute at Eli Braude's house. Recently, Motty had been failing a lot of tests and not doing his homework. Abba and Imma are really getting upset, thought Shevy.

Finally, Shevy thought about Tova, who lately was like a firecracker ready to explode. I can't stand it, she thought despondently as she stared vacantly into her math book.

After what seemed an eternity, the bell rang, and Mrs. Lipsett, the science teacher, came in for last period.

"Good afternoon!" chirped Mrs. Lipsett in her perpetually cheery voice.

Shevy groaned. Why does everyone have to be so happy when I'm so miserable?

Mrs. Lipsett went on happily, oblivious to Shevy's misery.

She announced gleefully, as if broadcasting the winner of a grand prize, "If you have your science books out, please leave them closed on your desks. We're having a little impromptu oral quiz!"

The girls groaned audibly. First the *Chumash* final and now a surprise quiz! Mrs. Lipsett was known for her impromptu quizzes. They always counted towards the final grade.

Later, when Shevy would recall what happened in class next, she would think of it as the dark black clouds that brought in the storm. A beginning of things to come.

Mrs. Lipsett took out her roll book and proceeded to quiz the class on the circulatory system. The girls were unprepared, and very few knew any of the answers. Their teacher's invariable cheerfulness seemed somewhat quelled today. Even Dinah didn't know many of the answers.

Finally, Mrs. Lipsett looked around at the girls and said, "Last question. I'm hoping *someone* here can answer it. We reviewed it two days ago! What are the two lower chambers of the heart called?"

She scanned the room once again. There was only one hand raised, Dinah's.

"That's it? Just one girl?"

Undaunted, Mrs. Lipsett called on several other students. Optimistic as always, she assumed that they probably knew the answer but were afraid to volunteer. Her assumption proved wrong, as every student she called on replied incorrectly. Defeated, she finally called on Dinah.

Dinah smiled and spoke confidently. "Atria."

Mrs. Lipsett sadly shook her head. "No, Dinah. Sorry. How about you, Shayna Leeba?"

Shayna Leeba blushed and her freckles stood out clearly on her face. "The ventricles," she said in a low voice.

Mrs. Lipsett gave a wide smile. "Excellent, Shayna Leeba! You are correct! But it seems to me that the rest of this class has a lot of studying to do."

Shevy stole a glance at Dinah. Dinah's face was bright red. Her hands were clenched into tight fists on her lap, and her lips were pressed together to form a grim white line. She was staring at the closed notebook on her desk.

Shevy turned her eyes away. She didn't like the expression she saw on Dinah's face.

After class was over, Shevy dragged her limp, drained body over to Rivkah and Ahuvah.

"You know, it seems like Shayna Leeba is giving Dinah a run for her money," Ahuvah was saying to Rivkah.

"Yeah. I know what you mean. Dinah was always the smartest in the class, no question about it. Now it seems that Shayna Leeba is coming in a close second. And who knows? They may even be neck in neck! Dinah doesn't seem too happy about it, either."

Shevy broke in on the conversation. "That's the understatement of the year, Rivkah. Dinah is really upset."

"What makes you say that?" asked Ahuvah.

"I know. I just do!" Shevy stated emphatically. "Sometimes her thoughts are printed on her face for a second.

This is definitely not the end of it. I just know it."

Rivkah and Ahuvah looked at each other. "What do you mean?"

"It's more than just not getting the answers right. Think about it. Then again, maybe don't think about it. I guess it's *lashon hora*."

Shevy went to the back of the room and put on her coat. It felt like it weighed a ton. "Anyway, I'm off. So long."

"Wait! I'm ready," called Rivkah, hurriedly collecting her books.

"Thanks, Rivkah, but I'm not very good company today. I'm in a miserable mood." Shevy opened the classroom door and left.

She dragged herself down the block to the bus stop, rode the bus in silence and then dragged herself home. Things were getting worse every day, she thought.

Shevy entered the house, dropped her coat without hanging it up and shoved her books on the hutch. In the kitchen, Tova was polishing a *Chanukah menorah*.

"Where is everyone? How's Imma feeling?" asked Shevy, as she started to wash the dirty dishes in the sink.

Tova looked up. "Hi! Imma's sleeping. Motty went to the Braude's to play with Eli. And those dishes you're washing are his, so leave them alone and let him clean up when he gets home. And you don't have to make supper. Abba is buying pizza. If you want to find Yehudah, I suppose you should find Imma. You know what I mean."

Shevy gave a wry smile. Since her mother had gotten sick, Yehudah just couldn't stay away from her any longer than he absolutely had to.

"How's Imma?" Shevy asked again.

Tova just shrugged her shoulders and resumed her *menorah* polishing. Despite her sister's words, Shevy finished washing the dishes and even washed off the counters. Then she went to the refrigerator, took out an apple and an orange and put them into a bowl. She extracted a box of cookies and a bag of popcorn from the pantry. Carrying her snack, she trudged up the steps and down the hallway toward her room.

Shevy was almost there when her foot struck a large, soft object. She felt herself pitching forward and shot out her hands reflexively as she fell to the floor. The popcorn and cookies went flying. Shevy hit the carpeting with a yell and was surprised to hear another cry that matched her own.

"Yehudah! What are you doing sitting in front of Imma's bedroom like that? I tripped over you! Now look at this mess," whispered Shevy ferociously.

Yehudah had his back against their mother's bedroom door and his feet sprawled out in front of him. In his lap, he had a pad in which he had apparently been busy coloring.

Yehudah looked up with his big blue eyes. "Sorry, Shevy. I'm just waiting for Imma to wake up."

Shevy exploded. "Why don't you leave her alone already? You're stuck on her like a leech! She can't go anywhere without you hanging on to her dress! Now you sit outside her door doing nothing while she sleeps! What do you think is going to happen if you go away for a second? Do you think that if you leave she'll . . ."

She stopped in mid-question, her mouth hanging

open, horrified by what she had been about to say. Morbidly, she wondered if Yehudah was really thinking the same awful thought.

Yehudah nodded his head in the affirmative, agreeing with his sister's unfinished statement. He stared at Shevy with trembling lips, a wounded expression on his face and his eyes brimming with tears. He soon burst out into sobs that shook his little body, the escaping tears running down his cheeks. He ripped up his papers and clenched them in his tiny hands.

"She needs me! Imma needs me. I'm taking care of her," he gasped.

Shevy lifted Yehudah in her arms and carried him to her room. She sat down beside him and put her arm around him. Yehudah snuggled up close to Shevy and continued crying in large heaving sobs.

Shevy felt awful. Here's my baby brother, she thought morosely, scared out of his wits, taking the burden of Imma's illness on his little six-year-old shoulders. And I have to say such a terrible thing to him! It's bad enough that I didn't realize what he was going through until now. Now I have to go and reduce him to tears?

I just can't do anything right, she thought miserably. Wherever I go these days, I just bring doom and gloom! All I ever do is think about myself.

She rocked Yehudah gently, telling him softly, "Imma'll be alright. You'll see. She'll be alright."

"Really, Shev?" asked Yehudah.

"Really, Yehudah," Shevy said, as much to herself as to Yehudah. "And you are doing a very good job watching her. You are the best boy an Imma could have."

"I am?"

"Yes, you're delicious, you are! When I become an Imma, I want a little boy just like you!"

She continued holding and rocking him until Yehudah finally stopped crying. Quick to change moods, he happily shared her snack. Shevy agreed to a game of Topple, and the two of them sat on the floor playing quietly.

After Yehudah won three rounds, Shevy stretched her back and said, "That was fun, Yehudah, but I'm going to sleep. You can stay here in my room if you want."

"To sleep? It's before supper! And tonight is Tuesday—don't you have play practice?"

"Yes, but I'm not going. I had an absolutely awful day and I'm tired."

"Aren't they going to yell at you if you don't go?"

"Maybe. But who cares. Hmm . . . as for the play, I know what I have to do, anyway."

"What?" asked Yehudah curiously.

"Umm, oh, nothing." Shevy crawled into her bed and pulled the bright pink cover over her head. Yehudah climbed into Tova's bed and put on her small lamp. "G'night, Shevy."

Shevy didn't answer. She was fast asleep.

5

The next morning, Shevy felt herself being gently shaken. With half-closed eyes, she saw the sun streaming through the sheer pink curtains. Tova was standing over her, fully dressed.

"Huh?" asked Shevy, closing her eyes again.

"Shevy, you're really late. This is the third time I'm waking you. I'm leaving for school right now!"

"I don't feel well. I'm staying home."

"What's the matter?"

"Nothing. I just don't feel well."

"Should I ask Rivkah to bring your homework?"

"No. I just want to sleep."

Shevy fell back asleep for several hours. When she woke up again, the clock showed 10:56 a.m. Slowly, she got out of bed, got dressed and *davened*.

On the way to the kitchen, she passed her parents' bedroom. Her mother was napping on top of the bed covers, fully clothed.

Shevy went downstairs, ate a late breakfast and cleaned the kitchen. Then she started on the living room. The floor was strewn with the remnants of Motty's latest art project.

I have to help out more in the house, she thought. I have to help out more and make it easier for Imma.

Shevy moved aside the couch, careful not to drag it on the carpeting. She plugged in the vacuum cleaner and was about to turn it on when her mother came down the steps, a worried look on her face.

"Hi, Imma, how do you feel?"

"*Baruch Hashem*. But why are you home from school, and what are you doing?"

"I wasn't feeling so great before, so I slept late. Now I'm cleaning up," answered Shevy with a smile.

"Do you feel alright now?"

"Yes."

"Good. Thank you for cleaning, but I'd like you to go to school now. I don't want you missing classes."

"But Imma, half the day is over," protested Shevy.

"So go for the other half," insisted Mrs. Feder.

Defeated, Shevy soon found herself on her way to school. It felt strange going at that time of the day. After entering the building, Shevy stopped in the office and put a sealed letter into Mrs. Levy's box.

In class, she sat at her desk, barely listening. All she could think about was how she could help more at home.

The school day was over. The room erupted in commotion as nineteen girls got ready to head home.

"Shevy, I'll call you tonight after dance practice," said Rivkah. "Okay?"

"Fine," mumbled Shevy, hunched over her book bag.

"Shevy, what is the matter with you today?" asked Rivkah, concerned.

"What kind of question is that?" Shevy asked, whirling around to face Rivkah.

"What do you mean, what kind of question is that? You came to school in the middle of the day without a word to anyone, and you've been acting upset ever since. You were in a bad mood yesterday, too. I'm your best friend! What's wrong?"

"Yeah? Well since you're my best friend, don't you think you should know why I'm upset?" Shevy retorted angrily.

"What is the matter with you? Why are you so angry? Is it because of the *Chumash* test?" Rivkah ran her fingers through her curls, bewildered.

"Yes! I mean, no! Rivkah, I got a 45 on the test. A 45! I failed!" Shevy banged her hand on the desk.

"Well, I'm sorry you did so badly," began Rivkah.

"Sorry's not going to help my mark!"

"Shevy, what do you want from me? I can't believe you, Shevy. I can't even understand you. What are you so angry about?" Rivkah stood with her hands on her hips, her eyes blazing.

Shevy banged her fist on the desk. "Why can't you understand me? I thought you were my friend!"

"Listen, I thought I was your friend, too, and I thought you were mine. Why don't you at least tell me what's bothering you? I know you well enough to see that it's not just the bad mark. It's something else, and I don't have the faintest idea what it is." Rivkah's features softened as she waited for Shevy to reply.

Shevy said nothing.

Rivkah threw her hands up in the air resignedly. "Well, I'm going home! I have things to do before dance practice tonight."

"Go, then. Who cares about me, anyway?"

"Shevy Feder! What do you mean by that? I care, for one! Look, you've been so upset that you even missed play practice last night."

"It makes no difference any more. I quit."

"You what?" screeched Rivkah.

"I quit the play."

"Why?" asked Rivkah incredulously.

"Because my mother was sick last night."

"What are you talking about? Why do you have to quit the play if your mother was sick last night?" Rivkah could not believe what she was hearing.

"She needs my help."

"But can't you still do both? Shevy, you've been waiting for this part for years! You can't quit now."

"I already did. I wrote a note to Mrs. Levy and put it in her box when I came to school today."

"What?"

"You heard me. I'm finished."

"Shevy, you're just upset today. It was a bad day. Please don't quit the play."

"Rivkah, you simply don't understand!"

"I'm trying to understand, if you would just explain yourself."

When Shevy finally answered, it was in a trembling voice. "Riv, I can't talk about it. It's something I've been

thinking about for a long time, but I can't say it. I can't tell
you or anybody. I'm sorry. Please forgive me."

She snatched her coat and left.

Rivkah stood glued to the spot, a puzzled look on her
face.

"What was that all about, Rivkah?" asked Ahuvah
curiously from the other side of the room.

"I wish I knew, Ahuvah. I really do."

Shevy got off the bus and ran all the way home. The
tears that had been streaming down her face had stopped
a little while ago. As she went up the walkway to the
house, she tried to wipe away any traces of her sorrow and
to look as normal as possible. Her face was set in a grim,
resolute expression as she quietly inserted her key into
the lock and opened the door.

"Hi, Shev," said Tova. "Why'd you use your key? You
usually knock."

"I didn't want to bother anyone to open the door for
me," answered Shevy.

Shevy put down her books, hung up her coat and
walked towards the kitchen. She took a quick look around.
What a mess! Motty had obviously feasted, and the
remains were all over the kitchen. He was sitting on the
counter, his back leaning against the refrigerator. A book
was propped up on his lap, and an almost-empty carton
of ice cream was in the crook of his arm.

"Hi, Shev," he mumbled between bites, looking up
from his book. "I'll clean up soon. Don't get upset."

"That's okay, Motty. I'll take care of it. Don't bother
yourself."

"You will?" asked Motty incredulously.

"Yes."

"Well, hey, I'm certainly not going to argue with you!" With that, Motty returned his attention to his book and ice cream.

Shevy peeked into the living room. Her mother was sleeping on the couch. Shevy sighed and turned back into the kitchen.

As she started cleaning up the table and getting supper ready, she noticed a note on the refrigerator. "Frozen pizza and frozen peas and carrots for dinner. Imma," she read.

As Shevy was pondering the note, Yehudah came sidling up to her at the refrigerator.

"What do you want, Yehudah?" asked Shevy.

"I'm thirsty. I need a drink."

"Sit down. I'll get it for you."

"You don't have to. I can get it myself."

"That's okay, Yehudah. I don't mind. Sit down."

Yehudah shrugged his shoulders and sat. Shevy served him a glass of iced tea and then took out some fresh vegetables and started peeling them.

"Hey! Why are you peeling those vegetables?" Motty protested, looking up from his book. "Didn't you read the note Imma left? Supper is all from the freezer."

"I read the note!" retorted Shevy. "I can read, too! If you read the note, why did you act like such a slob and stuff yourself with junk right before supper? Look at you sitting on the counter like that! Is that the right thing to do? And now you bug me because I'm peeling some vegetables for supper?"

"Okay, okay, take it easy. Do what you want. It makes no difference to me." Motty hopped off the counter and headed for the door.

Shevy stopped peeling. "Oh, Motty! I'm really sorry I said that! Please don't feel bad."

Motty looked at Shevy for a moment, a puzzled expression on his face. "Shevy, are you nuts or something? Do I look upset? What's the matter with you today, anyway?"

Before Shevy could reply, Tova walked in.

"Shevy, you don't have to peel vegetables," she said. "The note says pizza and frozen vegetables. There is no mention of fresh vegetables."

"I know what the note says! Why is everyone making such a big deal about these stupid vegetables? I'm just doing it because Imma likes vegetables."

Tova rolled her eyes in exasperation. "Well, sorry for asking! Motty, how did you do such a good job cleaning the kitchen so fast?"

"Umm . . . to tell you the truth, I didn't. I would have, uh, I might have . . . I was thinking about it, but along came Shevy and offered to do it for me! I didn't want to disappoint her or anything, so I accepted her offer."

"Shevy, you cleaned up after this guy?"

"Maybe. What if I did?"

"Oh, I get it," said Tova, a bitter edge creeping into her voice. "You're in one of your angel moods again. Little Miss Perfect, just in this world to serve and suffer, huh? Use the key instead of knocking, not to bother anyone. Clean up Motty's disgusting messes for him. Prepare supper even though it's my turn, and then peel vegetables even though you didn't have to. How noble! What self-sacrifice!"

Shevy's face turned bright red. "I think I'd better leave," she mumbled.

"No! I'm leaving! I can't stand it when you get into your holy moods!"

Tova stormed out of the kitchen, and Motty quietly slipped out, too.

Shevy stood motionless for a few moments, stung by Tova's words. She doesn't realize why I have to do this, she told herself.

She completed the preparations for supper and just finished setting the table when her father came through the door.

"Smells good in here! Hello, everybody!"

The Feder children greeted him, and Mrs. Feder woke up and came into the kitchen. Presently, the whole family sat down to supper.

"Thank you, Shevy, for preparing supper tonight. The salad is especially nice," said Mrs. Feder appreciatively.

Shevy managed a wan smile. "You're welcome, Imma. I thought you'd like it."

"Yes, I do. But why did you use the china? You could have used paper."

Shevy put down her fork. "Don't you like using real plates?"

"Yes, of course I like using real plates. It's just that paper is so much easier."

"Well," said Shevy, her face reddening, "I thought you'd like it."

"Shevy! I do like it. I appreciate it. I just don't see why you should have to work so hard if it's not necessary. Anyway, let's change the subject. Does anyone want to talk about their day?"

Everyone except Shevy seemed to have a lot to say. Mr. Feder spoke about a new project at work, and the children spoke about school. Yehudah, in particular, seemed to go on and on.

After everyone had had a turn, Mr. Feder turned to Motty and remarked, "Motty, it looks like you did a great job on those breakfast dishes. You must have even dried them, because I don't see a single dish in the drainboard!"

"Thanks, Abba!"

Tova threw a sharp glance at him. They both knew who had really done the dishes.

"Well," Motty cleared his throat, "I didn't really do them, Abba."

"You didn't?"

"No. Shevy did them."

"She did?"

"Yeah," said Yehudah, "And when I went to get a drink, Shevy made me sit down and she got it for me." Yehudah rolled his eyes, and Tova and Motty both snickered.

"Why is everyone picking on me tonight? What did I do that's so terrible?"

"Shevy," began Tova, "why do you think you have to . . ."

"Enough, Tova!" yelled Shevy, jumping up from her chair. "I don't need your advice! This whole thing means nothing to you!"

"Shevy, sit down and tell us what's the matter," said her father gently.

"I don't want to!" she exploded. "Nobody else understands what's really going on here! Not Rivkah, not my family, not anybody! And you guys are the meanest brothers and sister that anyone ever had!"

Shevy pushed her chair back, toppling it to the floor with a crash as she ran from the table. The Feders sat in stunned silence as they heard the loud clatter of her footsteps upstairs and her bedroom door slamming shut.

"What is everyone yelling about?" asked Yehudah.

"She's so weird lately!" added Motty.

"Shevy's going through a rough time," said their father softly.

"Poor Shevy," said Tova sarcastically.

"Yeah, poor little Shevy," added Motty in the same sarcastic tone. "Poor Shevy is too sensitive, that's what she is."

"Yes, she was very sensitive tonight!" agreed their father. "But that's a reason to be extra nice to her, not extra mean. I want all of you to be as nice as you can to her. If you can't think of anything nice to say, don't say anything at all."

Tova, Motty and Yehudah silently nodded their assent.

"Motty, you'll clean up after supper. Everything! It had better be spotless. But before you start, I'd like to speak with you in the den. I got a call from your school today."

Motty looked at his father, a nervous expression on his face. "Abba, I can explain that . . ."

"Good. Later. After supper. Tova, please pass the salt."

Tova did so, glancing at Motty as she did. He was staring down at the table, a worried expression clouding his face.

6

An hour after the Feders had finished their dinner, Shevy heard a knock on her door. She ignored it, and continued to do so as it was repeated. Finally, she heard a voice through the locked door.

"Shevy, it's Abba. Listen, Shevy, I expect you to be in the front hallway with your coat on in five minutes."

"I don't want to go anywhere."

"I'm not asking you. I'm telling you! Understand?"

"Yes," answered Shevy softly.

Five minutes later, Shevy and her father were exiting into the cold night air.

"We're going to Pizza Perfect," said Mr. Feder.

Shevy didn't answer, and they walked the few short blocks in silence. Presently, they entered the small pizza and ice cream store. It had just opened a few weeks earlier and was the first kosher eatery in town.

"What will you have?" asked Mr. Feder, as Shevy sat down at a corner table.

"Butter pecan," mumbled Shevy, studying the grain of the light blue formica table top that glistened under the strong fluorescent lights.

"Coming right up, my pretty."

Mr. Feder went to the counter to order and quickly returned. Shevy took her cone, made a *brachah* and licked the ice cream. She was in too miserable a mood to enjoy anything, even ice cream.

Mr. Feder had ordered a banana split, covered with lots of hot chocolate. He and Shevy sat in silence for awhile. He took a napkin from the table and folded it in different directions. When he was finished, he put it in front of Shevy. He had turned it into a duck.

"Very nice," said Shevy blandly.

"Well, I think it's a very fine likeness," said Mr. Feder, feigning insult.

Shevy didn't say a thing. She just sat there brooding.

"Shev, why don't you tell me exactly what is going on inside that lovely head of yours?"

"Not much. I don't know."

"Well then, I'll be more specific. Perhaps you can tell me why you decided to drop out of the play."

Shevy looked up with a start. "How do you know about that? Who told you?"

"You can ask me that later. First, I want to know why you dropped out."

"Well, I failed the big *Chumash* test today. I got a 45," said Shevy, staring at her ice cream cone.

"Yes?" asked Mr. Feder expectantly.

"What do you mean, yes? Aren't you upset with me? I failed!"

Tears started rolling down Shevy's cheeks. She angrily wiped them away and continued.

"And Imma feels sick today. You know why? Because of me! She went shopping with me two days ago for material for my stupid costume and wore herself out. And Tova had to take care of supper all by herself because I went with Imma. It's all my fault! If only I wasn't part of that stupid play, Imma would feel better now, I wouldn't have failed the test and Tova wouldn't have had to work so hard. And if only, if only . . . well . . . forget it!"

Shevy put her hand to her forehead, the tears coming down faster and faster, her face flushed a bright red. She dropped her half-finished ice cream on the table, not caring about the mess.

"If only what, Shevy?" her father asked softly.

"If only," whispered Shevy, "if only I was a better person, maybe Imma never would have gotten sick . . ."

Choked with sobs, Shevy could say no more.

Mr. Feder moved over to Shevy's bench and put his arms around her. Shevy hid her face in her father's sleeve and continued crying.

After a few minutes, Shevy's tears subsided. She slowly pulled herself away from her father and dried her eyes.

"You must think I'm a terrible person," she began miserably.

"I think nothing of the kind, Shevy. In front of me, I see a considerate person who always goes out of her way to help people. I see a person with whom everyone wants to be friends. You're not a terrible person, you're just feeling terrible. And it's certainly understandable.

"You are going through a very hard time," he continued. "It is not at all abnormal for a person in your situation to have all kinds of scary thoughts. You can't stop thinking about it all day and all night.

"But there's one thing you should know. It is absolutely *not* your fault that Imma is sick. Hashem did not punish your mother because of anything you did or didn't do."

"How do you know that, Abba? Maybe He did."

"Shevy, honey, Hashem does not punish one person for another person's sins."

"Really?"

"Really. Shevy, do you think that if you act really good now, Hashem will make Imma better?"

"Yes."

"I see. Is that one of the reasons why you didn't go to Ahuvah's house with Rivkah the other night?"

Shevy nodded.

"And is that also the reason why you dropped out of the play, so that you could help out in the house more, hoping that if you did, Hashem would make Imma better?"

Shevy nodded again.

"Shevy, look at me," said Mr. Feder deliberately. "It's not our job to decide how Hashem rules the world. It is only our job to do the best we can. We just have to try. That doesn't mean we have to do everything. You don't have to pass every test. You don't have to help with supper every night. You don't have to be perfect. No one is perfect. And if you make a mistake today, you have tomorrow to correct it.

"Hashem is like your father, too. He is your father in *shamayim*, and He loves you. A father would not punish your Imma because you failed a test or yelled at your brother. Understand?"

Shevy nodded.

"And so what if Tova did a little extra work? I'm sure that she was happy to do it for you!" He grinned wryly, and continued, "And even if she wasn't so happy, you're also entitled to a break once in a while!"

"As a matter of fact," he continued, "I think you've been taking far too much responsibility lately. When we get home, I'm going to shift the schedule a bit so that I can make life a little smoother for you.

"And one more thing," he added. "Even if Imma wasn't feeling so well today because of the mall outing, she was happy to go! Just like you like to make people happy, Imma also likes to make you happy. She loves you. Seeing you so happy that day more than made up for her tiredness since then.

"Shevy, believe it or not, it doesn't make Imma happy to see you working so hard because of her. She loves you and wants you to help her, but she doesn't want you to be miserable from doing more than you should."

Shevy seemed lost in thought. "You don't think that if I leave the play, it will make things better? That everyone will be happier?"

"No, Shev. We're all excited for you. We know how much you wanted the part. I'd be very sad if you dropped out of the play."

"And you're not upset that I failed that big *Chumash* test?"

"No. You're a very good student, and you always try your best. It happens every once in a while. Want to know something?" he smiled. "Once when I was in eighth grade, I got a seven on the final math test."

"A seven?" asked Shevy incredulously.

"Yup. A seven out of a hundred."

"And what happened?"

"Nothing! I failed. That's it. And now no one even cares or remembers."

Shevy sighed deeply. "Abba, I feel so much better now!"

"Good," said Abba, perching his glasses on the tip of his nose. He raised his spoon in the air and assumed a stern expression. "Now, ve vill have a test." He slapped the spoon on the table. Shevy giggled. "Iz it your fault zat Imma iz zick?"

"No," Shevy laughed.

"Vill Hashem make her to be better only iv you clean more dishes, vash more pots and get only von hundreds on zee tests?"

"No!"

"Very gut. And now, zee vinal question. Veel you pleeze to clean up zees butter pecan ize cream? It iz dripping on my pants and shooz."

"Oh, no!" Shevy exclaimed, jumping up and laughing as she cleaned up the spreading puddle, which was all that remained of her ice cream cone.

Mr. Feder helped her, and they left the store together. It was a cold night, and father and daughter tightened their scarves against the biting chill.

"Shevy, there's one more thing I want to tell you. You

can't always change the things that go on around you. You can't control what other people do. But you can control, to a large extent, the things that go on in your head. Your thoughts belong to you.

"Whenever you start thinking sad or angry thoughts," he continued, "just turn the dial. Like a radio. If you don't like one channel, go to the next. Try to focus on the good things in life. Think about how, thanks to Hashem, we have doctors who can cure Hodgkin's disease. Think of all the people who love and care for Imma, and that Imma will soon, with the help of Hashem, be feeling better forever.

"And when you don't want to think of the sickness at all, turn the dial again. Think of all the friends you have who care for you. Think of your nice school or your wonderful home."

"Or that I have such a nice Abba," added Shevy with a smile.

"Absolutely," said her father, grinning in return. "Absolutely."

"Or that I'm going to be in the play."

"That's the idea. Whenever you're feeling sad, just turn the dial."

"I'll try, Abba, but I just don't know if I'll be able to do it."

"Try, Shevy. It might be hard at first, but just keep on trying."

Shevy's face took on a serious expression. "You know, Abba, I think I made a whole lot of people angry at me today."

"Oh?"

"Yes. I guess I'll have to take care of it."

"Hmmm."

"Abba! I love you. Thank you."

"Shevy, I love you with all my heart. You are an extra special person to me."

7

"**B**ecause," said Dinah emphatically, her eyes flashing and her cheeks reddening, "it's just not right!"

"What's not right?" asked Rivkah, who had just come into the classroom. She took off her coat and stamped the snow off of her boots.

"Dinah was just talking about Shayna Leeba," explained Shani.

"Well, what about her? What did she do?" asked Rivkah.

"It's not what she did, it's what she thinks!" said Dinah, tapping her forehead for emphasis.

"Well then, what is it that she thinks?" asked Rivkah.

"She thinks she's better than us!" answered Shani pointedly.

Rivkah sighed. This was not turning out to be a good week, she thought. On Tuesday, Shevy had lost her temper, and things hadn't been the same between them since then. On Wednesday, Shevy had wanted to apologize, but Rivkah was too sore about the way Shevy had acted to even want to listen.

Then Shayna Leeba had done better than Dinah on a math test, and the teacher had made a big deal about it in front of the class. Dinah, in an unusual display of assertiveness, had waited until after class and riled up the girls against Shayna Leeba. She called her a show-off, a *frummie* and a general pain in the neck. Rivkah had tried to defend Shayna Leeba but had only gotten yelled at for her trouble.

On Thursday, Shevy hadn't even tried to talk to Rivkah and had worn a pained expression on her face all day. In an effort to avoid the previous day's unpleasantness, Shayna Leeba had refused to answer any of the teachers' questions. This only served to make Dinah angrier than ever.

To top it all off, Rivkah had made what felt like a thousand mistakes at dance practice during lunch. Mrs. Levy had lost her patience and had cut the practice short by fifteen minutes.

Today, *baruch Hashem*, was Friday, thought Rivkah, and if things didn't go well, at least it was only half a day of school. On the other hand, trouble was certainly brewing early today. Dinah was starting it before Rivkah even had a chance to take off her coat.

"Are you listening, Rivkah? I was talking to you."

"Please, Dinah, spare me the details. There's no reason for you to get so upset at her! She's a new kid. She has no friends. She's shy. And she certainly isn't smart just to annoy you!"

"Well, she thinks she's better than us! I don't mind that she's smart, just that she's so haughty about it!"

"Haughty? Shayna Leeba? You must be kidding!" said Rivkah, running her fingers through her brown curls.

"Why? We're just trying to tell it like it is," replied Dinah. Most of the girls were in the classroom by then, and everyone was listening intently.

"Like what is? When did Shayna Leeba ever tell you that she was better than you?" asked Rivkah.

"She doesn't have to say anything," Dinah retorted. "You can just tell by how she acts. She hardly talks to any of us and always keeps to herself. When did she ever come to one of our houses? For that matter, when did she ever invite one of us over to her house?"

Many of the girls nodded their heads in agreement. "It's true, Rivkah," agreed Ahuvah tentatively.

"I can't believe you guys! Did any of you ever invite her?" Rivkah looked around. The girls slowly shook their heads. "Maybe she's too shy to invite any of us. We haven't exactly been welcoming. She's the one who's new here. We should be going out of our way to make her feel at home."

Dinah looked around the room. She saw that she was losing ground and didn't plan to give up yet.

"Well, how *can* we invite her?" she asked. "Don't you remember the *Chumash siyum* last week. She wouldn't eat the cookies because they weren't *yashan*."

"Yeah," agreed Shani. "And she wouldn't even drink the soda because she said it wasn't a *heimishe* brand."

The class erupted. Everyone had something to say about this.

"Oh, stop it!" Rivkah called out loudly. Everyone turned around.

Rivkah looked really upset. "So what? So what if they do things differently? What's wrong with keeping *yashan*, with only eating certain brands? Just because you don't do it doesn't mean it's wrong. After all, all of our families have different customs. Shayna Leeba's family is just a little stricter than most. Would you want her not to listen to her parents just to make you happy?"

"That's not what I'm saying!" insisted Dinah, looking around the room to gauge the response. The girls were listening quietly, still apparently unconvinced by either Rivkah or Dinah.

"Dinah," said Shevy slowly, "remember the girls from public school who came to us for a *Shabbaton*? Would you want them to think that you're strange because you keep *mitzvos* that they don't?"

"That has nothing to do with it! There's a big difference. What Shayna Leeba's doing is just too much! She's strange and that's that!" Dinah sat down at her desk, a stubborn look on her face.

"Dinah, you're just jealous," said Ahuvah quietly.

Dinah's face reddened and her eyes narrowed. "That's not true, Ahuvah, and you know it!"

Ahuvah lifted her eyebrows in a questioning manner but didn't say anything further.

"You think you know it all, don't you?" asked Dinah vehemently.

"I'll tell you one thing I don't know, Dinah," said Ahuva.

Dinah crossed her arms. "Oh yeah? What's that?"

"Where *is* Shayna Leeba? She's the only girl absent today."

"Sick," said Shani derisively. "I was in the office when her mother called in and said that Shayna Leeba will be late. She supposedly wasn't feeling well last night."

"Can't miss a day of school, can she?" asked Dinah to no one in particular.

"I'll tell you one last thing, Dinah," said Rivkah. "You're real smart, and you can get a lot of people to agree with you whether you're right or wrong. Personally, I think people should think for themselves. On the other hand, if they're going to follow you, then you'd better be real careful about what you say. You have a real responsibility!" she concluded, somewhat louder than she had intended.

"Well, I thank you for your speech," said Dinah with a sarcastic smile. Several girls giggled.

Just then, Mrs. Krigsman walked in, and the girls' conversation came to an abrupt halt.

"*Boker tov*, girls. Please take out your *siddurim*, and we will begin."

"Psst, Eli, come here a minute." Motty Feder pulled Eli Braude into the school's boiler room.

"What? I can hardly see in this place. There's no light," protested Eli.

"Come on." Motty led Eli to the room's only window and pulled a small brown bag out of his pocket.

Eli peered inside. "Big deal, Motty. It's only four dead mice."

"That's what you think, Eli, but listen closely."

Motty whispered his plan and Eli's face lit up in a wide grin.

"Hey! This is even better than when we set off those firecrackers during lunch."

"Much better," agreed Motty with a wink.

When the bell rang for recess, Shevy turned to Rivkah. "Rivkah?" she asked, but there was no response. She tried again. "Rivkah?"

"What?" asked Rivkah, not looking up from the book on her desk.

"I just wanted to say that I'm sorry for being so nasty the other day."

"It doesn't matter," answered Rivkah flatly.

"Great!" said Shevy brightly. "You were really brave just now, sticking up for Shayna Leeba."

"Yeah," answered Rivkah, her nose still buried in the book.

"Do you want to come to my house after school today?" asked Shevy brightly.

"I don't think so, Shevy. I have a lot of things to do before *Shabbos*."

"Rivkah, I told you I'm sorry. How many times do I have to say it? Why are you so angry?"

Rivkah finally turned around. "I'm not angry, Shevy, I'm just confused. I don't feel like talking about it now. Okay?"

A hurt look crossed Shevy's face, but she said no more.

During recess, Shevy kept thinking about Rivkah's anger, about her mother's illness and about how she was going to tell Mrs. Levy that she wanted to be back in the play. All three topics were sources of stress.

Shevy tried her father's idea. She mentally changed channels and thought about her pretty play costume and about the birthday party that Leah was having next Sunday. But the topics she tried to avoid kept creeping back into her mind, and she hardly heard Mrs. Lipsett asking her to bring a box of supplies to the teachers' room.

While Shevy trudged down the steps, she dropped the heavy box on her toes and yelled out in pain. Perfect, thought Shevy, as she picked up the load and flung open the door of the teachers' room. The perfect start to a perfect day.

"Oh!" she said, startled. "Mrs. Krigsman! I didn't know anyone was in here. I'm sorry I banged the door so loudly."

"Hi, Shevy. That's okay. I'm glad you're here. I wanted to talk to you anyway."

Shevy swallowed hard. "The *Chumash* test. I know that I failed, but . . ."

"The *Chumash* test?" Mrs. Krigsman looked at her quizzically. "Oh, no. I don't want to talk to you about that. You've always been a good student. That test was just an exception, I'm sure."

Shevy leaned against the door and sighed in relief.

"I really wanted to ask you about your mother. I was so sorry to hear that she's sick. You know, we were in the same high school. She was in twelfth grade when I was in ninth."

Shevy nodded. Her mother had told her about that

once after Mrs. Krigsman had come to visit her in the hospital.

"She was in charge of the school's *chessed* organization and did an excellent job. She always knew what each person needed. Believe it or not, I used to be very shy. Your mother constantly went out of her way to greet me or stop to chat, even though she was a senior and I was just a freshie. I remember it to this day."

Thoughts of her mother brought tears to Shevy's eyes.

"Shevy, I'm sorry. Why are you crying? Are you scared about your mother?"

Shevy nodded her head.

"Shevy, sit down. I want to tell you something," Mrs. Krigsman said. "When I was young, I was sick a lot. I had a very bad case of asthma, and the medicines I took for it made me weak and disoriented. I was prone to infection and often stayed home from school. I thought I'd never get better. Even the doctors weren't really sure of what to do.

"The nights were the worst. Those terrible nights!" Mrs. Krigsman continued in an animated voice. "How I remember them! Night after night I sat in my mother's room wheezing from asthma and crying in fear. One time, my mother suggested that we say some *Tehillim* together. I found it surprisingly comforting. To this day, whenever I'm nervous, afraid or sad, I always say a *perek* of *Tehillim*."

Mrs. Krigsman looked at Shevy and smiled.

"You see, when I say *Tehillim*, it's my way of saying, 'Hashem, please take care of me.' It always comforts me, Shevy. Maybe you should try it too."

"I guess I could try."

"Good. And I've been *davening* for your mother. Ever since I found out that she wasn't well, I have her in mind when I *daven*. I'm sure that soon, with Hashem's help, she'll be better."

Mrs. Krigsman squeezed Shevy's arm affectionately.

"Any time you'd like to talk, about anything, I'll always be here for you."

She looked at her watch. "I'd better go now. My Shmueli's coming home from school soon, and it's almost *Shabbos*."

With a parting smile, Mrs. Krigsman gathered her books and escorted Shevy out of the office. On the way out, Shevy almost bumped into Ahuvah.

"Ahuvah! What are you doing here?"

"I was looking for you. What did Mrs. K. say to you?"

"Boy! She's something else," said Ahuvah after Shevy filled her in. "In class she's a tyrant, and out of class she's like a regular person."

Shevy laughed.

"Anyway, I have something to tell you," said Ahuvah. She plopped down on the stairs and continued. "Last night my aunt called. Guess what? She had a baby girl! My parents left early this morning to Cincinnati, and they're staying there until Sunday night. My grandparents are coming to stay at our house to be with us. I can't wait! My grandparents are terrific. It'll be so much fun! I'm making a *melaveh malkah* tomorrow night. You have to come. Okay?"

"Umm . . . I don't know. I think so. I'll have to ask my parents."

"You have to come!" repeated Ahuvah. "You really do."

"Why do I have to come?"

"Because I just invited Shayna Leeba."

"What? Wow! That was really nice of you, Ahuvah!"

"I guess. But you know me! First I do, then I think. I really want it to go well, which is why I want you to be there! What if I say the wrong thing? You know how things just fly out of my mouth. It must be my red hair!"

"Are you sure it isn't your mouth rather than your hair?" asked Shevy with a grin.

"Very funny, Shevy Feder!" Ahuvah gave a flip of her head that shook her wavy, carrot red hair over her fully freckled face.

Shevy laughed. Last week, when the *bikur cholim* ladies had come around looking for volunteers to visit at the hospital, Ahuvah had immediately volunteered her services seven days a week, fifty two weeks a year. Just yesterday in Math class, she had knocked over her chair as she jumped out of her seat, yelling out the correct answer so loudly that the teacher almost kicked her out of the room.

"Don't worry, Ahuvah, you'll be okay."

"I hope so. Oh, by the way, I also invited Rivkah."

"Uh-oh," said Shevy.

"What is that supposed to mean?"

"It's just that Rivkah is really upset with me. I don't think she's going to want to come."

"Oh," mused Ahuvah. "No wonder."

"No wonder what?"

"Well, it's just that I was surprised when Rivkah didn't

agree right away. You know how Rivkah loves parties."

Shevy looked sad. "I don't think that Rivkah will ever be my friend any more," she said, biting her lip.

"Shevy, you worry too much. Of course, Rivkah is going to be your friend. Rivkah can't stay angry at anyone for too long."

"I guess this will be the first time."

Ahuvah punched Shevy's arm. "Cut it out. You'll see. It's only Friday morning now. I predict," announced Ahuvah, her eyes closed and her index fingers touching her forehead, "that before *Shabbos* even starts, everything will be terrific between both of you."

"Thanks, Ahuvah *Haneviah*."

"You're quite welcome! And since you're my friend, there will be no charge."

"How utterly kind of you."

"Don't mention it! Anyway, I'm expecting to hear from you before *Shabbos*. You had better come!" Ahuvah looked at her watch. "Hey, we'd better hurry. The next class is about to start."

"I still have to get my books," said Shevy, jumping up. "You go ahead. I'll be there soon."

"Hurry, because *dinim*'s next, and if we're late, we'll definitely suffer the consequences."

"Okay!" yelled back Shevy, running down the steps.

On her way back up to class, Shevy had just finished calculating mentally how many days were left before her mother was to be readmitted to the hospital, when . . .

BANG!

"Look what you did!" screeched Dinah.

Shevy quickly looked up. She saw Dinah looking

furious and Shayna Leeba's face red with embarrassment. On the floor between them was a pile of books,
strewn about haphazardly.

"Dinah, I'm sorry, I didn't see you. I'm late enough as
it is. I didn't want to come late to *dinim*, too."

"Yeah? Well, you dropped all my books, they landed
on my snack, and now it's crushed. You'd better pick
everything up now!"

"Really, Shayna Leeba," called Dinah's friend Shani
from the back of the room. "You should really be more
careful."

Shevy turned towards Rivkah and the two exchanged
a glance of despair. Shayna Leeba's face flushed again,
this time with anger. But she didn't say a word as she bent
down and started picking up the books.

Instantly, Rivkah jumped to her feet. "I'll help you,
Shayna Leeba," she said, as she bent down and scooped
the books together. Shevy saw a grateful look pass over
Shayna Leeba's face.

"Sticking up for your *frummie* friend?" asked Dinah.
"It's no surprise. The two of you deserve each other."

Rivkah stood up to her full height, her eyes flashing.
"Listen, Dinah, just cut it out. Here are your books and
here's your snack." Rivkah thrust the items into Dinah's
arms.

"Sheesh! Take it easy, Dinah!" exclaimed Ahuvah.
Dinah just shrugged her shoulders and went back to her
seat.

The class knew that Shayna Leeba was just as smart
as, if not smarter than, Dinah, and that this seemed to
infuriate Dinah. Dinah constantly found opportunities to

belittle Shayna Leeba, and Shayna Leeba had continued to take the abuse in silence.

Shevy glanced at Dinah. She was rearranging her books, and though her face wore a gloating smile, Shevy could see a sad, vulnerable look beneath the surface. Suddenly, Shevy felt sorry for Dinah. And she sensed that the worst was yet to come.

8

𝒯he last bell of the day rang, and Rivkah quietly
packed up her books and started home. Kicking
a rock along the sidewalk, she thought about how confus-
ing life had become.

Since Tuesday, when Shevy had gotten so angry at
her, Rivkah had been thinking how much Shevy had
changed since her mother's illness had begun. She was
unpredictable and moody. It was understandable, of
course, but Rivkah didn't know how much more of it she
could take.

All of my trying to be nice is getting me nowhere, she
thought. Maybe I should quit trying while I'm behind.

Walking into her house, Rivkah was greeted with a
loud screech of delight from her two-year-old sister,
Shulamis. Rivkah scooped her up in her arms and carried
her to the kitchen.

"Hi, Ma," said Rivkah.

Mrs. Akerman was removing a large tray from the

oven. "Hi there! How was school today?" she asked.

Rivkah set Shulamis down on a chair. "School was fine. But . . ."

"But what?" asked Mrs. Akerman, as she slipped another pan into the hot oven.

"But I don't know what to do about Shevy," Rivkah said in an exasperated tone. "I'm going nuts!"

"One minute." Rivkah's mother handed her a bag of potatoes and a peeler. "I'm a bit behind schedule for *Shabbos*. You peel and talk, and I'll make a salad and listen."

She sat down and started cutting tomatoes. "Okay, Rivkah, what's going on?"

Rivkah talked rapidly as she peeled. "Well, earlier this week, Shevy got a really bad mark on her *Chumash* test. You know Shevy, Ma, she always does well. Anyway, she was upset. I tried to talk to her, but she started yelling that I don't care about her. Then she told me that she quit the play."

"She did?"

"Yes! Can you believe it?" Rivkah looked up momentarily from the pile of peels and potatoes. "She's wanted that part for years! But it's not only that. It's . . . it's just that ever since her mother got sick, Shevy's been so unpredictable. Everyone in school knows it. I wouldn't tell Shevy, but some of the girls kind of avoid her. They're afraid she's going to get upset over nothing. I guess they're also afraid that they might say the wrong thing to her."

Rivkah put down her peeler and took the bowl of potatoes to the sink. Mrs. Akerman started cutting mushrooms, and Rivkah continued to speak.

"The teachers make special allowances for her. She's so much in her own world, I'm sure she doesn't even realize it. I don't know what to say to her. I don't even know what she wants half of the time. Sometimes what I say makes her smile, and sometimes the exact same thing makes her upset!"

"Uh-huh," said her mother. "Go on."

"I want to help her but don't always know what to say to her. And when I don't, she gets mad at me. That drives me nuts! It's almost not worth it to be her friend."

"It sounds like you're angry at her."

"I am!" Rivkah washed the potatoes furiously. "I guess I really am angry at her. After all, just because her mother is sick doesn't mean she can go around acting like she does. It's like she doesn't care about anyone's feelings but her own."

After a pause, Rivkah continued. "Then I get angry at myself. Here her mother is sick and goes to the hospital all the time. Their atmosphere at home is so different! It's just strange over there. Mr. Feder is always so smiley and everything, but you can tell that his mind is on other things.

"So when I remember that, I get upset at myself," she explained. "I tell myself that I should be nicer to Shevy. But it's so hard. Today Shevy came over and tried to apologize again. I was so upset, I wouldn't even let her. Now I feel like a creep." Rivkah shut off the water and began cutting the potatoes.

"Shevy probably feels bad for what she did to you," said Mrs. Akerman softly.

"Yeah, I know. But she should have thought about that before."

"Well, Rivkah, what do you want to do?"

"I'm not sure. I guess I still want to be her friend. I wouldn't want to leave her when she needs me most. Besides, I do like her. But I don't know what to do."

"I'm glad that you still want to be her friend," said her mother. "She needs your friendship now more than ever."

"But I never know if I'm saying the right thing or not!"

"Don't worry about that. If you don't know what to say, don't say anything. Just listen. I'm sure Shevy has a lot of people who are able and willing to give her good advice. But she only has you as a best friend. Listening and sympathizing are the best things you can do for her."

"Just listen?"

"Yes. Just listen."

Rivkah pondered this advice. "I guess that sounds good. But what should I do when she gets so upset and angry?"

"Just remember that she's not angry at you," answered her mother. "She's upset at what is happening to her."

"Does that mean that she can just say whatever she wants, and I have to put up with it?"

"No. When she goes too far, you should tell her, although it's probably better to wait until she calms down. But you should definitely explain to her that it bothers you."

"Good."

"But remember," Mrs. Akerman added, "that because she's in a difficult situation, you're going to have to put up with a lot. You have to realize that."

"I guess so," said Rivkah in an uncertain voice.

"Don't look so forlorn," her mother said, smiling. "It's a great *mitzvah*. It's true *ahavas Yisrael*. You're helping out a friend in need when it's most difficult to do so. I'm sure Hashem will repay you many times over."

Rivkah gave a small smile.

"Rivkah, if anyone can do the job, it's you! You are naturally nice and friendly and always go out of your way to make people happy."

"Oh, Ma! You're embarrassing me."

Mrs. Akerman laughed. "Okay, I'll stop. I'll finish making the *kugel*. Please give Shulamis and Chesky their baths for *Shabbos*."

"On the other hand, Ma, embarrass me," said Rivkah with a grin. "It's better than working!"

Rivkah had just finished taking Chesky and Shulamis out of the bath when the phone rang. She ran down the hall to get it, leaving the two dripping kids wrapped in towels.

"Hi," said a familiar voice. It was Shevy. Rivkah felt a twinge in the pit of her stomach.

"Just a sec."

Rivkah took the phone into her parents' bedroom and closed the door behind her.

"Okay, we can talk now," she said.

Shevy spoke quickly, one word running into the next. "I just wanted to tell you that I'm sorry I was so mean to you earlier this week. I can understand if you don't ever want to be my friend again, but I just wanted to apologize one more time. That's it. It's up to you now. I don't know what else to say," she concluded.

"Shevy, it's okay, really."

"It is?" asked Shevy, suddenly bewildered.

"Yes, it is."

"Really? That's great! I was feeling so awful. I thought that you wouldn't want to be my friend any more. I don't know how I could have coped these last few awful months without you!

"But I understand why you got so angry," she continued. "I've been really mean to you for quite some time."

"Well, I have to admit, it's kind of true," said Rivkah softly.

"I know, and I'm really sorry. Okay?"

Quick to change the subject, Shevy asked, "Are you going to Ahuvah's on *Motzei Shabbos*?"

"I forgot all about it! I guess so, but I have to ask my mother," said Rivkah.

"I asked mine and she said okay. I'm really glad that Shayna Leeba's coming."

"Yeah, that was nice of Ahuvah to invite her."

"Well, you sure stood up for her in class today, Rivkah."

"It makes me really upset when Dinah starts up with her. Shayna Leeba never did anything to Dinah. Why is Dinah being so mean? The worst thing is that Dinah gets so many of the other girls to agree with her. I just can't understand her!

"Anyway, I'd better stop," Rivkah added quickly. "It's *lashon hora*, and besides, I left the kids in the bathroom wearing nothing but towels."

"See you tomorrow night!" said Shevy.

"Bye!"

Rivkah returned to the kids and dressed them in pajamas, humming a merry tune all the while.

"Hey! Whatchu' boys doin'?"

Eli jumped. It was Mr. Peters, the school custodian.

"We were just leaving," said Motty.

"Leaving? School's been over for an hour! You missed your bus for sure."

"That's okay, we'll walk," said Eli.

"Humph. Well, hurry up and get along now," he said crossly. "I have to mop the hallway."

Eli and Motty left hurriedly.

Together they walked down the hallway, their shoes clicking in the empty school building. As they turned the bend, Motty glanced over his shoulder.

Mr. Peters was standing there, a mop in one hand, a washcloth in the other and a curious expression on his face.

9

"**Bi!**" said Ahuvah excitedly, opening the front door and escorting Shevy and Rivkah in from the cold outside air. "I can't believe you came. I mean, of course I can believe you came, it's just that I'm excited. Oh, there I go again. Anyway, Shayna Leeba isn't here yet. Just remember, if I start to say anything stupid, kick me." Ahuvah hung up their coats and walked them into the kitchen.

Shevy and Rivkah laughed. "Don't worry, Ahuvah, you'll be fine," said Rivkah.

"I hope so. Anyway, Shevy, would you help me frost the cake? I'm trying to make a design, and I don't know how. You're much better with these things."

Shevy took over the cake decorating chore as Rivkah and Ahuvah looked on. Ahuvah had prepared three different colors of frosting, and Shevy concentrated on making the large round cake as pretty as she could. She drew pink flowers with long green stems around the perimeter. In the middle, she outlined the shape of a bird and started filling it in. Everyone was watching so closely that they almost jumped when they heard a knock on the door. Ahuvah ran to answer it.

"Shayna Leeba! Come on in! Let me take your coat. Look at the cake Shevy is decorating! It's almost finished."

"Shevy," said Shayna Leeba admiringly, "it's really beautiful!"

Shevy blushed. "Thanks!"

"Ahuvah," said Shayna Leeba, "I brought you a present."

Shayna Leeba smiled shyly and handed Ahuvah a small package.

"You did? You didn't have to do that! Rivkah and Shevy didn't."

Shayna Leeba's smile disappeared.

"Oh, don't listen to me," Ahuvah rushed on. "It was great that you brought it. Thanks a lot! Really."

She opened the present. "Hey! It's great. Look, it's a needlepoint set."

"I hope you like needlepoint," said Shayna Leeba.

"I do! I do! Thanks!"

"You're welcome."

Shevy put the final touches on the cake, and then the girls sat down to a delicious *melaveh malkah* meal. They feasted on pizza, french fries, salad, chocolate malteds, and, of course, the cake.

At first the conversation was stilted, but slowly and surely the ice broke. Soon Shayna Leeba and the other girls were talking as if they had all been friends forever.

"Math!" said Shayna Leeba, rolling her eyes. "It's my worst subject! I can never get it the first time. My father has to explain each problem about a hundred times before I understand what's going on."

"Your father?" asked Ahuvah.

"Yes. Why are you so surprised? Doesn't your father help you with your homework?" she asked, puzzled.

"I just thought that your father was learning Torah all day," said Ahuvah. "I didn't think he knew anything like math."

Shevy kicked Ahuvah under the table, and Rivkah just rolled her eyes and shook her head.

"What?" asked Ahuvah, genuinely perplexed. "What did I say wrong?"

Shayna Leeba just laughed, her blue eyes sparkling and lighting up her face. "Ahuvah, is that what you think? That my father leaves the house before we wake up, runs off to go learn and doesn't come home until after we go to sleep? And that he can't add or read English? And that my mother never sets foot out of the kitchen and only speaks Yiddish?"

"Well, not exactly that, but something like it."

"Oh brother, Ahuvah, you're really something!" exclaimed Rivkah.

"Actually," laughed Shayna Leeba, "my father does learn all day, but we see him at night, and he always helps me with homework, especially math. He's actually terrific at it. In high school, a teacher tried to convince him to go to college so that his talent wouldn't be wasted. My father told the teacher he didn't want his talent to go to waste either, and that's why he was planning to learn full-time."

"Really?"

"Really."

"Oh." Ahuvah seemed a bit overwhelmed.

"That's why we moved here from New York," continued Shayna Leeba in her soft voice. "My father joined the *kollel* here. He learns in the morning and teaches high school in the afternoon. My parents like living here very much."

"What about you?" asked Shevy curiously.

"Well, I miss New York. I had a lot of friends there."

"Yeah, and you didn't have Dinah making your life miserable," said Ahuvah impulsively.

Shayna Leeba's face fell. "It's not that bad," she mumbled.

Shevy was incredulous. "How can you say that? She's really out to get you, and she seems ready to get the rest of the class to go along with her!"

Shayna Leeba looked at Shevy for a few thoughtful moments, as if pondering what to say. Finally, she took a deep breath and spoke.

"I used to take things a lot harder, and get much more upset. But you see, my grandmother lives with us and she's really had a hard life. She was in a concentration camp and lost almost her whole family. Only one daughter survived—my mother. My grandmother never spoke much about it until last year. Then once she started, she could hardly stop. I guess that put things into perspective for me."

Shayna Leeba twirled her braid and looked sheepishly at the other girls. They were looking at her, afraid to speak for fear of saying the wrong thing.

Shayna Leeba continued in a lighter tone. "I want to thank you again for inviting me here, Ahuvah. That was really something special."

"Do you mean that this is the first time this year that you were invited to anyone in the class's house?"

Shayna Leeba blushed and nodded her head.

Once again, Shevy was shocked. "Shayna Leeba, you're really something! It must have been awful enough having to leave your old school only one year before graduation, and now, you have such a rough time here with everyone being so unfriendly!"

Shayna Leeba waved her hand dismissively. "Well, I can't say I feel great about it, but it's really no big deal."

The conversation never continued, because at that moment, the doorbell rang. When Ahuvah opened the door, she found both Shevy's and Shayna Leeba's fathers standing there. They were in the middle of an animated discussion, and the girls soon found out that the two men had known each other from their school days.

As it turned out, Mr. Feder and Rabbi Weinberg were *chavrusas* for years, until they both married and went their separate ways. They were overjoyed that they were living in the same town. They quickly made plans to continue where they had left off and learn together often.

On the way home, Rivkah and Shevy sat in the back seat of Mr. Feder's car while he happily recounted his days as a student. Shevy, however, was deep in thought.

She thought about the difficult time Shayna Leeba must be having. Every day of school must feel like time served in prison to her. Yet Shayna Leeba made it seem like nothing was wrong.

Then Shevy thought about her own situation. She felt
angry with herself for constantly dwelling on her own
problems, and she was disappointed in herself for not
being able to hide her feelings.

Maybe, she thought, I can be more like Shayna Leeba.
Maybe I can also make believe that all of my problems
don't matter.

10

"**S**it down! Sit down! How many times do I have to say the same thing?"

"But Mr. Cassaro, it stinks in here," Moshe said, holding his nose.

"Yeah, ugh! Let's go out to recess!" screamed Avi.

"Someone open the window!" yelled Chaim from the other side of the room.

Sweat glistened on Mr. Cassaro's forehead. This was his first year as a math teacher. Keeping control was never easy, but today was impossible! There was a persistent foul stench permeating the classroom, and pandemonium was breaking loose. Mr. Cassaro cleared his throat.

"I'm giving zeros to any boy who does not open his math book. Now!" A couple of boys opened their books.

"Danny, get out of the closet!"

"But Mr. Cassaro, the closet doesn't smell!"

A mob of boys charged towards the closet.

"Sit down. All of you! This minute! Danny! Moshe! Rafi! Take out paper and do the problems on page 158. Now!"

Giggling, Danny and the rest of the boys exited the closet and sat down. Most of the class opened their books.

Mr. Cassaro wiped his brow. It isn't exactly quiet, he thought, but at least they're sitting!

Had Mr. Cassaro been more observant, he would have noticed two boys in the back of the room. They sat near each other, watching the chaos but not participating in it. From time to time, they whispered to one another or exchanged secretive smiles.

They were, of course, Motty and Eli.

"Washington or Hershey Park, the choice is yours," announced Mrs. Krigsman. She closed her *Chumash* and arranged her papers and books.

"I know how much the eighth grade looks forward to the graduation trip. Therefore, this year, I am going to allow you girls to decide where you want to go! It's still early in the year, but a bit of advance planning has to be done.

"I'm leaving the room so that you can decide by yourselves. You have ten minutes. Write your choices on pieces of paper and pass them to . . ." Mrs. Krigsman looked around the room. "Shayna Leeba, come on up. You lead the discussion and collect the papers."

Shyly, Shayna Leeba walked to the front of the room as Mrs. Krigsman exited.

Shayna Leeba spoke softly. "I guess everyone should give their opinion."

Ahuvah quickly spoke up. "I think Hershey Park is best. I've never been there. I've been to Washington twice, and a third time would be bo-o-o-ring!"

"I want Washington. My brother went there and he said it's great," Shani chimed in.

The discussion quickly turned into a shouting match. Everyone was yelling at once, and no one heard anyone else. Shayna Leeba kept asking for quiet, but no one even looked in her direction.

During a momentary lull, Dinah spoke up. "Hey, Shayna Leeba, what's the matter with you? Didn't Mrs. Krigsman tell you to lead the discussion? Can't you do anything right?"

The class sat in shocked silence. Dinah's voice dripped with such venom that everyone was momentarily taken aback.

Ahuvah quickly jumped up. "That is a disgusting thing to say, Dinah. You apologize right now!" Ahuvah's eyes were flashing and her hands were shaking.

The rest of the girls also seemed pretty upset with Dinah. Even Shani, Dinah's best friend, sat silently, not saying anything in her defense.

Dinah sat there calmly. "I will do no such thing, Ahuvah. If Shayna Leeba couldn't do the job, she should have said so from the start."

Some of the girls started shouting at Dinah, berating her for what she said. Shevy looked at Dinah and once again saw that look of vulnerability. Although Dinah's face was set in a look of calm determination, her eyes betrayed her true feelings of fear and uncertainty.

Ahuvah was still fuming. "Listen, Dinah, if you don't

apologize right now, this whole class will . . ."

"It's okay, Ahuvah," interrupted Shayna Leeba, her face a deep red. "It doesn't matter."

"It does matter! If Dinah doesn't apologize in the next ten seconds, we'll . . . we'll put her into *cherem*, just like people did years ago. That means that no one will talk to her or have anything to do with her until the end of this year."

"Yeah," agreed Sarah. "Enough is enough! Say you're sorry, or it's *cherem* for you, Dinah."

Dinah just sat there and shrugged her shoulders indifferently. Several girls began a rhythmic chant, "*Cherem, che-rem, che-rem.*" Their chanting grew louder until Ahuvah had to shout over the din.

"Okay, Dinah, it's your choice. What's it going to be?"

Before Dinah had a chance to answer, Shevy jumped up from her chair. "Stop it! Stop it! You're all getting carried away. Leave Dinah alone! Okay, she said something nasty. You think this *cherem* nonsense will help?"

"Who cares whether it will help? We just don't want to have anything to do with people like that!" Leah declared vehemently.

"You're all ganging up on one person," Shevy continued. "That's worse than what Dinah did!"

"What's with you all of a sudden, Shevy?" asked Leah. "If you feel so strongly about it, then why don't you go into *cherem* with Dinah?"

"Fine with me!" yelled Shevy.

Rivkah spoke in a calm voice. "Everyone stop it. No one is going into *cherem*. All of you just stop acting like a crazed mob!

"Now let's get back to what we're supposed to be doing! Take out your pieces of paper and write down your votes. There's only two minutes left until Mrs. Krigsman comes back."

It seemed as if Rivkah had knocked the wind out of the girls. Their frenzy stopped as quickly as it had started. They quietly took out papers and wrote down their votes.

"Well," said Mrs. Krigsman, breezing into the room and collecting the papers from Shayna Leeba, "it seems that I made a wise choice in trusting you girls to come up with this decision in a calm and adult manner."

The instant class ended, Dinah picked up her coat and books and left the school building in a hurry. Shevy glimpsed her leaving the room and impulsively ran after her.

"Wait up, Dinah! I can't catch up with you," shouted Shevy breathlessly.

Dinah stopped running and waited for Shevy to join her.

"Shevy, it was nice of you to stick up for me before," she said, "and I thank you, but could you just leave me alone?" Dinah's face was tear-streaked.

"Dinah, just tell me one thing. Why do you hate Shayna Leeba so much?"

"Oh, come on, you know why already," said Dinah bitterly. "I think you've heard me speak on the subject often enough. She's haughty, she's a know-it-all, she's also . . ."

"You know what I think?" interrupted Shevy. "I think you're jealous."

"Jealous? Of her? Are you nuts?"

"You are jealous. Because she's smart, just like you."

"I know she's smart. How could anyone not know, when everyone crowds around her desk all the time? And she's so nicey-nicey, it's sickening!"

"Just 'cuz she's smart, Dinah, doesn't make you any less smart. Besides, what's the difference who's smarter? Everyone likes you anyway. They'd like you even if you weren't smart."

"Who are you kidding, Shevy? The only time anyone talks to me is when she's asking me for help."

"Dinah! That's not true! Don't you have friends? Isn't Shani your best friend? And besides, the reason that everyone likes asking you for help is because you're so nice about it and so patient."

Dinah sighed. "Shani is my friend, but that's it. There's no one else."

"Dinah, that isn't true. You're such a nice person! Everyone likes you! I like you."

"You do?"

"Yes! Why is it so hard for you to believe?"

"Because . . ." she hesitated. "it's hard for me to make friends. The only reason I'm so friendly with Shani is because I've known her since we were babies. I didn't have to work at becoming friends with her."

"Dinah, I'm sorry it's so hard for you. If you just tried a little, you'd be friends with a lot of the other girls."

"I don't know, Shevy. Do you really think so?" Dinah asked tentatively.

"I know so!"

Dinah shrugged her shoulders skeptically. "Well, I can forget about it now," she said. "Everyone hates me!

They wanted to put me in *cherem*, remember?"

"Dinah, by next week the *cherem* stupidity will be half forgotten. Just wait and see," said Shevy.

"I don't know, Shevy, I just don't know."

"That's about all I can tell you, Rabbi Alpert," the plumber said as he snapped his toolbox shut. "I've checked all the pipes, and there's nothing there. It's not the plumbing. I don't know what else to suggest."

"Hmmm. Well, it has to be coming from somewhere." Rabbi Alpert ran his fingers through his graying beard.

The odor was getting steadily worse. In his twenty-eight years as principal, he had never confronted a situation quite like this. The windows were all opened despite the cold weather, and air fresheners hung on every classroom wall. But still the odor remained.

It was a small building, Rabbi Alpert thought. The classrooms and offices were all on the same floor. The combination lunchroom/auditorium downstairs offered the only respite from the smell.

The gas company had sent someone. A cleaning service had come. A construction worker had been called. Now a plumber had investigated the problem. They had all left shaking their heads.

Rabbi Alpert leaned back against the hallway wall and thought. The smell had started on Monday. On Friday afternoon, he remembered, Joe Peters had seen some boys lingering for a long while after school. Joe had said that it looked as if they were up to no good. It was time to talk to Joe again.

11

Rivkah gripped the armrests of the dentist's chair tightly. Her fingers were white, her eyes squeezed shut and her heart beat so loudly she could hear it pounding in her ears.

"Rivkah, you're doing fine! This filling will be done in half a minute."

Dr. Braunstein lifted up his drill and turned it on by stepping on the floor switch. The loud whirring noise made Rivkah's heart beat faster. She was sure she'd faint any second.

"Ow! I feel it! The novocaine is not working, 'cuz I feel it."

Dr. Braunstein rolled his eyes at Shevy, who was standing at her friend's side. "Bubala, you can't feel it. I haven't even touched you yet!"

Rivkah groaned, and the dentist began his work. Shevy placed her hand in Rivkah's and Rivkah squeezed so hard that Shevy's hand began to tingle. After what seemed an eternity to both girls, Dr. Braunstein was finished.

"You're all done. It's over."

"*Baruch Hashem!*"

"So, you want a sticker?"

"Very funny," said Rivkah.

Dr. Braunstein chuckled to himself as Rivkah leaped out of the chair and left the office as fast as her legs could carry her.

Rivkah opened the door to the outside air and skipped down the steps. "It's over! It's over! I'm safe for another six months. Thanks for coming with me!"

Shevy laughed. She had been keeping Rivkah company at the dentist since they were both in sixth grade. Each time she went, Rivkah was more terrified than the last.

The two girls walked on, discussing the play, graduation, and Dinah. A week had passed since that awful *cherem* incident in class. It was never spoken about, but there was a certain chill in the air when Dinah was around.

"You know, Shevy, it's strange," Rivkah said thoughtfully. "Dinah was trying to get everyone to hate Shayna Leeba and like her, but the opposite has happened. Poor Dinah! Everyone seems to have turned against her."

Rivkah turned to Shevy. "Except for you, Shev. You've been so nice to her lately. Aren't you angry at what she did?"

"Not so much. I think she was only being so mean to Shayna Leeba because she feels like she lost her place in the class."

"That's no reason to do what she did."

"Maybe so, but she's really very insecure. That's why she's been acting like she has."

"How do you know that?"

"I don't want to get into it, Rivkah, but I just know. Believe me, she really needs us to be her friends, not her enemies."

"Well, it's hard to be nice to such a mean person."

"And since when is *ahavas Yisrael* only for people who act pleasantly all the time?"

Rivkah punched Shevy's arm playfully. "Since when did you become such a mature adult, huh?"

"Very funny, Rivkah. Look, I'll tell you something. I'm only telling you this 'cuz you're my best friend, so don't make fun of me, okay?"

Rivkah nodded.

"You know how I'm always thinking, crying and talking about my mother being so sick?"

"Yes, but you've been much better lately, Shev," Rivkah added quickly.

"Yeah, I guess I'm getting there, slowly but surely. But anyway, you always stood by me, even when I was crying all the time, even when I was ignoring what was happening to you and was mean to you. I'm sure it wasn't easy, but you were—and still are—always there for me."

Rivkah blushed and Shevy continued. "But Rivkah, you stay by me because you're such a good friend. You understand what it's like in my house and what's happening to my mother."

"And?"

"Well, I think that situation is what helps me understand Dinah. The same kind of thing that makes me the way I am makes her the way she is."

"Huh?" Rivkah was confused.

"She only started being this way since Shayna Leeba came to school. Dinah is only mean to her because of the unusual situation, not because she's naturally mean. And that's why we have to go out of our way to be nice to Dinah in return."

"I don't understand you completely, but I sort of get the idea."

"I don't think I would have understood Dinah if my mother wasn't sick. Does that make sense to you?"

"I guess it does."

"Well, as my Abba says, you have to find good in everything Hashem gives you."

"Come in, Motty," said Rabbi Alpert. Motty walked in and faced the principal, who was leaning forward in his chair and drumming on the desk with his fingers.

"How's school, Motty?" he began.

"Fine, Rabbi Alpert."

"Fine, hmmm? Well, I have your *Gemara* test here in front of me, and as far as I know, a fifty-three is a failing mark. And yesterday I was told that during science you climbed out of a second story window and down a tree. Is that so?"

"I guess so," said Motty.

"You guess so." Rabbi Alpert put the test down on his desk and leaned back in his chair. "Let me tell you something that you won't have to guess about. Sit down!"

Motty sat.

"It's very simple. One more failing test in any subject, or one more wild antic, and you'll be suspended from school. Do you understand that?"

"Yes," said Motty meekly.

"Good. Now tell me back in your own words what I just said."

Motty hid his fear and forced himself to reply calmly, "If I fail or make trouble, I'm suspended."

"Exactly. Now let me ask you something else, Motty. Have you noticed anything sort of different in this school lately?"

"Different?" asked Motty, an innocent expression on his face.

"That's right."

"Well, I suppose it smells a bit strange."

"So I've noticed. Now tell me, Motty, is there anything you'd like to tell me about that?"

"Tell you?"

"That's right. About the smell."

"I can't think of anything."

"Do you know Joe Peters?"

Motty blanched, but only for a second.

"Yes."

"He told me that he saw two boys, one of whom looks just like you, hanging around the building after school a little more than a week ago. Was it you, Motty?"

"Yes, it was."

"And?"

"I was getting stuff ready for the science project."

"With Eli?"

"Umm, yes, with Eli."

"So . . . all of a sudden, you're very serious about science. How interesting!"

Rabbi Alpert paused, searching Motty's face with his eyes. "That's all for now. You may leave."

12

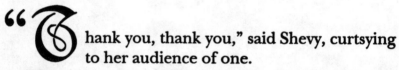

"hank you, thank you," said Shevy, curtsying to her audience of one.

"That was wonderful!" said Mrs. Feder, clapping vigorously.

"Oh, Imma! I can't wait for the real thing."

Shevy plopped into a kitchen chair and looked closely at her mother. Mrs. Feder was wearing a light blue sweater that softened her features. Shevy thought that her mother was looking very well.

Simmering on the stove was Shevy's favorite meal. Meatballs and spaghetti made by none other than her mother.

Impulsively, Shevy gave her mother a hug. "Imma, the play is fantastic, supper smells great and you look wonderful!"

"Thank you for the compliment! And now, for the finale, could you please call the other kids down for supper?"

No sooner was everyone seated around the table when the phone rang. Tova answered it and passed it to her mother.

"It's Tante Elly," whispered Tova.

Shevy rolled her eyes. "Yeah. You know what that means. She wants us to come stay with her when Imma goes to the hospital."

Mrs. Feder was scheduled to go into the hospital on Wednesday and stay through Friday. Mr. Feder usually stayed with her. Nearly always, the Feder children ended up staying at Tante Elly's house.

The kids loved Tante Elly, but they didn't like staying at her house. She always went out of her way to make them feel at home, but they always felt so acutely that they *weren't* home. When their mother was in the hospital, home was the only place they wanted to be.

"That was Tante Elly," said Mrs. Feder, hanging up the phone. "She wants you kids to go to her house when I go into the hospital."

"We don't want to go to Tante Elly's," began Shevy, looking at Tova for support.

"You don't? I thought you liked her so much," said Imma.

"We do. But we want to stay home. Here," said Tova.

"Yeah," agreed Yehudah, "it'll be fun! We'll have a party and make popcorn, and of course we'll do our homework and clean up. Okay, Imma? Can we?"

"Who'll take care of you? And Motty . . ."

Ten minutes later, after Abba entered the kitchen, the negotiations were completed. It was decided that Yehudah would play at a friend's house until one of the girls could pick him up. Everyone promised to be on their best behavior, and Mrs. Feder told each of the girls to invite a friend to stay over and help. Tova and Shevy readily agreed.

"So it's settled. I'll call Tante Elly as soon as supper is over and tell her," said Mrs. Feder.

Shevy hungrily slurped the long, luscious strands of spaghetti covered with a sloppy meat sauce and thought about the week.

Today was Monday, and in only two more days her mother would be going into the hospital. As usual, she would feel sick and tire easily for another week or so after that. Fear gripped Shevy, and she quickly turned her thoughts to the sleep-over that they would have when her mother went away.

A sudden pain in her arm made her glance up sharply.

"Ow!" Shevy turned around. "Motty! That hurt! Why'd you punch me?"

"I just tapped you. You were off in dreamland again. Anyhow, I wanted to know if you would do the dishes for me tonight. I want to go over to Eli's house."

"Well, I guess I can do it before I go to Rivkah's. Yeah, okay."

"Great! Thanks. You're the best sister!"

"She-vy," whined Yehudah. "Would you clear the table for me tonight? I'm sooo tired."

"Well . . ."

"Please? Please?"

"Well, okay."

Shevy looked at Tova, who had her eyes half closed

and was shaking her head in disgust.

"Shevy," said Abba in a warning tone.

"What?" Shevy thought for a moment, then realized what her father had in mind. She put down her fork, stood up and faced both of her brothers.

"Motty, if you think for one second that I am going to do the dishes for you tonight, you may as well forget it. Go do them yourself! And you'd better do a good job this time!"

Motty looked stunned.

"And Yehudah! You're not a baby! Clear the table with your own two hands."

Tova stood up, climbed on top of her chair and began clapping and bowing in Shevy's direction. When she was finished, she sat down with a grin and continued her supper. Mr. Feder sat back in his chair and shook with laughter.

Shevy turned towards her father, who was still laughing and wiping his eyes. "Great," she said. "Now that that's settled, I'm going to Rivkah's house to practice the play. Mr. Akerman said he'd take me home afterwards." Shevy tossed her head and skipped out of the kitchen.

"Abba," protested Motty as Shevy left the kitchen, "did you hear what she said? And how she said it?"

"Well, as a matter of fact, I did hear what she said and how she said it."

"How come you were laughing then? I just asked her for a *chessed*. Don't you always tell us that we should do *chassadim* for each other?"

"Yeah," agreed Yehudah. "And the Chafetz Chayim said to do *chessed*. We learned about him today in school."

Mr. Feder burst out laughing again.

"What's so funny?" sputtered Yehudah.

Mr. Feder smiled as he explained. "In this case, if Shevy did your dishes, it would not be a *chessed*. You just wanted to weasel your way out of it. As far as I know, it's not a *chessed* to teach someone how to weasel out of things. Don't you agree?"

"But I have homework, and I wanted to go to Eli's house!"

"Motty, that's just an excuse, and you know it. Right?"

"Well . . ."

"Well, nothing." Mr. Feder looked at his watch. "Oh my!" he said exaggeratedly. "Look at the time! Motty, I'm sure you'll want to do the dishes right away. That way you'll have ample time to do your homework with Eli. Yehudah, since you're so tired, you'd better clear the table immediately so that you can go to bed soon."

Motty groaned and looked at Yehudah resignedly, but slowly the two of them got up and did their respective jobs.

Motty had his coat on and was about to leave the house when he heard his father's voice. Turning around, he saw him coming down the steps, a paper in his hand. Motty recognized it and his face turned red.

"I met your science teacher today on my way home."

"Abba, I can explain that."

Mr. Feder didn't say anything but lifted his eyebrow in a questioning manner.

"I studied the wrong chapter. It was a mistake," explained Motty weakly.

"Motty, this is happening too often. Mr. Solaff also

told me that you're constantly late for class."

Motty stood there shifting uneasily from foot to foot. His father allowed the silence to linger a while before he spoke again.

"Did you do your homework yet?"

"Umm, well, I was going to do it at Eli's house."

"Close the door, Motty. You may not go to Eli's house tonight until this test paper is corrected and your homework is done and I've checked it. Is that understood?"

"Yes, Abba," replied Motty meekly, taking off his coat.

At the Akerman house, Rivkah and Shevy went up the staircase and into Rivkah's room. Rivkah shooed out two of her sisters, pushed aside a pile of toys and flopped down on the bed.

Taking out their books, the girls began studying. After twenty minutes, Shevy suddenly slammed her book shut and dropped it on the floor.

"Rivkah, I just can't think! Who cares about atoms and molecules when all I can think about is my mother going to the hospital? There are a million knots in my stomach!"

Rivkah didn't know what to say. After all, she realized, who *could* care about studying when their mother was so sick? But instead of changing the topic or saying something that she knew wouldn't help, Rivkah just nodded her head and waited for Shevy to continue.

"She's so sick when she comes home from the hospital. I can only imagine how sick she is when she's actually in the hospital. Sometimes it seems as if she'll never get better. It's just so scary. I can't stop thinking about it."

"Uh-huh," said Rivkah tentatively.

"My father keeps telling me that I should replace the bad thoughts with good ones. I'm getting better at it, but it doesn't always work."

Shevy shook her head and fingered the lace on the edge of the bed.

Rivkah was about to speak when Shevy picked up her book and opened it.

"Thanks for listening. I think I feel a lot better now."

"You do?" asked Rivkah, surprised.

"Yup, I really do. Okay, let's get going with Chapter Four."

The next night, Shevy lay in bed thinking, gazing through the open window. The streetlights gave her a good view of the gently falling snow. She snuggled up under her comforter and thought about tomorrow, the day when her mother would be going to the hospital.

Shevy tried in vain to stop the tears from rolling down her face. She turned towards Tova's bed. It was empty. Tova had a midterm the next day and was downstairs studying. Shevy twisted a long strand of hair around her finger and tied it into a knot. Haltingly, through her tears, she whispered a *perek* of *Tehillim*.

There was a knock at the door. "Yes?" asked Shevy.

"It's me," said her mother.

"Come in, Imma."

Her mother entered the room. She was wearing a long, flowered button-down robe.

"Hi, Shev. Can I sit with you?"

Shevy nodded, and her mother sat down on her bed.

She held Shevy's hand in one of her own.

"You're scared about tomorrow," said Mrs. Feder, gently pushing back Shevy's long hair.

Shevy nodded again. "I'm sorry, Imma."

"What are you sorry about?"

"For upsetting you by crying."

Mrs. Feder smiled. "You can cry all you want. Sometimes it's good to cry."

Shevy and her mother were quiet for awhile. Finally, Shevy asked, "Imma, aren't you scared?"

"Yes, Shevy, I'm very scared. It used to be overwhelming. It's gotten a lot better, though."

"What do you do when it gets bad?"

"Well, I try a lot of things. But there is one thing in particular that helps me a lot."

"Can you tell me?"

"Yes. You can even do it with me. Okay?"

"Okay."

"Good. Now close your eyes."

"Uh-huh."

"Alright. This is what I do. I say to Hashem: Hashem, I am so scared! All these frightening things are happening to me, and I have no control over them. I have to go to the hospital. I have to take strong medicine that makes me sick. I have to get shots and undergo tests. I'm dependent on so many people—the hospital staff, the doctors, the nurses. They are the bosses over me. But deep down, I know that You are the real Boss. Hashem, You control everything, and I control nothing. Please, Hashem, all these worries are too much for me. I am entrusting them to You."

Mrs. Feder looked at her daughter. Shevy's eyes were closed and tears were rolling down her face. Her mother continued in a whisper.

"Then, in my mind, I take out a big beautiful box and some very pretty wrapping paper. Hashem, I say, I am putting all my worries into this box. Please take my worries from me and take care of me.

"Then I wrap it beautifully, tie it up with a bow and send it off to Hashem."

Shevy opened her eyes and smiled through her tears. "That was nice, Imma."

"We're not finished. The hard part is next. You see, after that, I clear my mind of worries and try to put all my *bitachon* in Hashem. That last part used to take me a long time but not any more. I have learned that Hashem is the Master and that we have no control over the future.

"Then I do the easiest part! I think of all the good things I have, all the things for which I'm thankful. When I do that, I can't help but feel happy."

"What do you think about, Imma?"

"I think about what a nice family I have. I have a terrific husband and wonderful children. Not only do I love them, but each one has special *midos* and strengths. I think about my friends who are so kind and giving. When I think of all the people who are doing the best they can to help me, it fills me with gratitude. My list goes on and on! What are some good things that you could think of to help you, Shevy?"

"Let's see. I could think of Rivkah and all my friends at school and about the play. I could think of the family, too. I realize how much you and Abba mean to me. I don't take you for granted as much as I used to. I realize that parents are precious.

"You know," Shevy continued, "I think that since you got sick, I've become more understanding. Remember how I told you about Shayna Leeba? Well, she is different from the rest of the class, and I think there was a time when I wouldn't have wanted to have anything to do with her. I've come to realize that she's just a person like the rest of us. In the end, I learned a good thing from her!"

Shevy pulled the covers up to her chin and held her mother's hand. The two of them sat there, each lost in her own thoughts. Before long, Shevy fell asleep and her mother contentedly watched Shevy's rhythmic breathing.

"Shevy, you and I are so alike," whispered Mrs. Feder to the sleeping girl. "We both worry too much."

13

"**M**otty, it's getting really bad. Enough is enough!" whispered Eli vehemently. Motty and Eli were sitting next to each other in the noisy dining room.

"It is pretty awful," agreed Motty, as he popped one potato chip after another into his mouth.

"It's been a couple of weeks since those mice started stinking up the place. In case you haven't noticed, this school is in chaos."

"I know. I know. Listen, I never told you about what went on the other day in Rabbi Alpert's office. I'm really in over my head this time."

"Uh-oh," replied Eli.

"Listen! Remember the *Gemara* test we took last week? Well, I kind of failed. And remember when I went down the tree in science class? Rabbi Alpert found out. He told me that if I pull anything else or fail any more tests, he'll suspend me from school. And to top it all off, I think I failed the English test we took today."

"Great. Just wait until your father finds out."

"That's the understatement of the year. He hasn't been too happy with me lately as it is. If he found out that I put four dead mice in the school's hallway ceiling, he'd . . . he'd . . . who knows what? But he's sure to find out sooner or later, because Rabbi Alpert already suspects that it was us who hid the mice."

Eli groaned. "Okay, boy wonder, what are we gonna do about those mice? I'm getting really nervous. What a stupid idea that was! We can't even get back into the ceiling because Rabbi Alpert is staying late every day to work on the school dinner. Half the school board is there with him."

"Yeah, and the dinner isn't even till next month. By then we'll have to come to school with gas masks!"

Motty crumpled up his potato chip bag and thought some more. "We can't come in the morning, either, because Rabbi Alpert unlocks the place. We'll have to think of something."

"How about coming in at night? We'll get the keys somehow."

"Not a chance, Eli. The place is wired in fifty different ways. If I have to be suspended, I'd rather not pass the time in jail. We'll just have to keep thinking, Eli, or my goose is cooked," Motty said.

"Well, you'd better think fast, Motty, really fast, because guess who just walked into Rabbi Alpert's office?"

"Uh-oh, it's Mr. Applebaum. I'll bet he has my English test in his hand, and he's showing it to Rabbi Alpert!"

"What are you going to do?"

"How should I know? With this test and the mice incident, it's only a matter of time until the ceiling caves in. Ha-ha," said Motty wryly.

Motty looked distraught. He bit his lip nervously and shook his head. "You know, he can't suspend me if I'm not here. Right, Eli?"

"What do you mean?"

"I'll tell you later. Let's go."

"No, we didn't!" declared Shevy.

"Yes, we did!" asserted Rivkah, looking down at the counter.

"Well, since none of us can remember, why don't we just put in half," suggested Ahuvah.

"Great!" agreed Shevy.

"Okay," said Rivkah half-heartedly. "But I'm telling you, we already put it in."

Shevy, Rivkah and Ahuvah were mixing batter for cupcakes and were trying to remember whether they had put in sugar. Ahuvah poured in the agreed upon half measure of sugar and started the mixer whirring again. Over the din, she announced, "This was a great idea."

Shevy smiled as she washed her doughy hands in the sink. Tonight was the first night of her mother's hospitalization. The three friends had come home from school after picking up Yehudah from his friend's house. When they had arrived at home, Motty was already there, and Tova had arrived with her friend Naadia a short while later.

After the Feder children and all of their friends had shared a supper of hot dogs and french fries, Shevy and her friends had started talking about the upcoming play. The rest of the children left the room quickly, knowing that once any eighth graders started on that subject, it would be hours until they tired of it. Sure enough, hours later, the girls were still talking about the play while they baked.

Shevy returned the flour to the cabinet and saw her mother's wedding ring lying in her ring box nearby. She suddenly felt very sad. Poor Imma, thought Shevy, what are they doing to you now in the hospital? More of that awful chemotherapy that makes you so sick?

"Shevy . . . Shevy!" called Ahuvah.

"What?" asked Shevy, coming out of her daze.

"Where are the cupcake holders?" asked Rivkah.

"Here."

Shevy reached up into the closet and handed them to Ahuvah.

"You know," said Rivkah as she poured the batter, "we should bring some to Shayna Leeba tomorrow."

"That's a great idea," agreed Shevy.

"I guess it's okay," said Ahuvah in a dull voice as she licked the spatula.

"Why do you sound like that?" asked Rivkah.

"Like what?" asked Ahuvah defensively.

"Like you'd rather not bring her anything," said Rivkah.

"Oh. Well, I don't mind if you bring her some cupcakes. I mean, why not? It's really nice. I was just thinking . . . Oh, forget it."

"What?" insisted Rivkah. "Spill the beans."

"Fine!" said Ahuvah, a little louder than she intended.

"It's just that, well . . . I was thinking of what Dinah was saying about Shayna Leeba. I mean, why *does* she have to be so different from everyone? Why does she have to always act like the world's greatest *tzaddekess*?"

Shevy and Rivkah looked at each other in bewilderment.

"Ahuvah!" yelled Rivkah.

"I know. I know. You think I'm being terrible."

"I just think you're listening to Dinah too much. Didn't we all have a good time when she came to your *melaveh malkah*?" asked Rivkah.

"Yes. I guess so."

"Don't you remember what Dinah did to her that day in class when her books fell down? And when we planned the class trip? That was really mean," said Rivkah.

"I guess so. I suppose you're right."

"Ahuvah, it's not like you to talk like this!" said Rivkah sharply.

"Yeah, yeah, you're right. Anyway, enough said on the topic. Put the cupcakes in the oven so we can eat them!"

Several hours later, the cupcakes were eaten, the kitchen was cleaned and Ahuvah was fast asleep on the living room floor. Nearby, Shevy and Rivkah sat across from each other in the quiet living room.

"Shevy, it was really fun tonight."

"It was, Rivkah. I had a good time."

"How's your mother?" Shevy and Tova had called the hospital a short while ago.

"She seemed okay but tired. Those medicines knock her out. I also spoke to my father, who was his usual cheerful self. Only tonight and tomorrow night, and then they'll be home."

"Do you ever get to go see her there?"

"No. You have to be fifteen to go upstairs. The first time she was there, my father talked the doctors into letting me go in. That was my first and last time. Tova goes every month. She told me that she doesn't stay long because Imma is half asleep from the drugs they give her."

"Do you want to go?"

"I do and I don't. I guess if I really wanted to go, Abba would get me in. I'm halfway scared to go. Abba said that it's okay, that I shouldn't feel bad if I don't want to go, so I just don't go at all."

"Oh," said Rivkah meekly.

"Anyway, I really feel okay this time. I'm trying to put it out of my mind and leave it up to Hashem."

"Do you say that *perek* of *Tehillim*?" asked Rivkah.

"Uh-huh."

"You know, you're terrific, Shevy."

Shevy blushed.

"Really, it's true," she said softly. "Months ago you wouldn't even be able to say a word about your mother without falling apart, and now you're really managing well."

"Thanks, Rivkah." Shevy paused. She was reluctant to continue, but the darkness of the room and Rivkah's patience encouraged her to go on.

"Remember the night of that *melaveh malkah* with Shayna Leeba," said Shevy. "Talking to her helped me. Here was Shayna Leeba having such a terrible time in school, and she was able to accept it with a smile! Why shouldn't I do the same?

"Really, though, a lot of it is just a show," said Shevy with a sigh. "I'm still always thinking about my mother. What if she doesn't get well? What if she . . . well, you know. My mind just doesn't stop. But I guess I've just learned to control everything a little bit better."

Shevy and Rivkah talked into the night. The silvery moon shone through the sheer white curtains and a small light seeped in from the kitchen. They spoke about anything and everything as the minutes ticked by. Finally, the two girls drifted off into a deep, quiet sleep.

Two days later, *Erev Shabbos*, the Feder children ran around the house, cooking and cleaning as fast as they could. They had refused all offers of help, and now the race was on with less than two hours until *Shabbos*.

"Motty! Yehudah!" Tova yelled upstairs. "Come down! Hurry up!"

Motty and Yehudah trudged down the steps.

"Yeah?" asked Motty.

"Listen. This is emergency time. Yehudah, you clean the living room, and Motty, you peel the potatoes."

"Tova, I just finished vacuuming upstairs! Besides, where is Shevy?"

"She's cleaning the bathroom. Hurry up! Abba and Imma are almost home."

"Okay, okay."

Before long, the cooking was done and the whole house sparkled. All that was left were some last odds and ends in the kitchen. Shevy and Tova were cleaning the counters when they heard the key turn in the lock.

Everyone ran to the front door.

"Abba! Imma!" yelled Yehudah. "Hi! We got everything ready for *Shabbos*!"

Their mother smiled wanly as their father said, "Great, Tova! Please take this suitcase upstairs."

Shevy looked at her mother. She looked pale and sick. She was walking very slowly, as she trudged up the steps.

Shevy quickly turned around and ran back into the kitchen. Presently, Tova joined her, and they quietly continued cleaning.

"Tova," said Shevy after a brief silence, "she looks so sick. Her face is so white."

"Yeah. Well, pass me the Ajax."

Shevy whirled around and slammed the Ajax down on the counter. "Here! Here's the stupid Ajax! Okay?"

Shevy ran from the kitchen and up the steps, totally missing the surprised look on Tova's face.

Shevy knocked on her parents' door. "Come in," called her father.

Shevy opened the door.

"Hi, Shevy," said her mother softly, her voice barely audible.

Shevy walked over to her mother's bed. She leaned over and tenderly stroked her cheek.

"Hi, Imma. We're glad you're home. You'll feel better real soon."

Her mother gave a weak smile and squeezed Shevy's hand gently. "Sit down next to me for a while, Shevy," she said, her voice low and indistinct.

Shevy sat down and softly rubbed her mother's back.

Mrs. Feder's eyes were closed, but she still held on to Shevy's hand.

"Nechami, I have your pills ready. Sit up for just a second," urged Mr. Feder.

Wordlessly, Mrs. Feder sat up and took the pills, quickly swallowing them with a glass of water. Almost immediately, her head fell back onto her pillow. Minutes later, she was asleep. Mr. Feder motioned to Shevy, and the two of them tiptoed out of the room.

"Abba," Shevy whispered. "She looks so sick. Sicker than ever before."

"Yes, I know. She had a bad time with the medicine. They changed her dosage a bit."

"They made a mistake?"

"They guessed wrong."

"Guess? How can they guess with something like that?"

"Shevy, they do the best they can. Doctors are not infallible."

"When will she be better?"

"It will be like all the other times, Shevy. It will just be the first day or two that will be really bad. I promise you, she'll be better real soon."

Once again, Shevy felt tears coursing down her face. Her father put his hand around her. "Shevala, Shevala," he said in a soft, crooning tone.

Shevy dried her cheeks with the back of her hand. "It's okay, Abba. You don't have to worry about me."

Mr. Feder kissed Shevy on her forehead and gave her a hug. "I'm going downstairs to see what else has to be done for *Shabbos*."

Descending the stairs, Mr. Feder heard angry voices coming from the kitchen.

"You forgot to buy the soda, Motty!" said Tova loudly.

"So what? Big deal. Why do you care about it so much?"

"Because I do! On *Shabbos* we always have soda and now we don't. Put on your coat and go get it. Now!"

"Tova, it's freezing outside! We have apple juice, we have orange juice, we can even make lemonade. Stop being such a crazy!"

Tova suddenly flopped down on to a chair and burst into tears.

Motty threw his hands up in exasperation. "Alright, alright, if it means that much to you, Tova, I'll get the stupid soda. What kind do you want?"

Tova just shrugged her shoulders and continued crying. Motty shook his head and started out of the kitchen. On the way, he met his father.

"You know what, Abba?" he asked.

"What, Motty?"

"Girls can be really weird. Really!"

Mr. Feder gave Motty a wink and went into the kitchen. He opened the refrigerator, took out a slice of cake and sat down at the kitchen table. He made a *brachah* and quietly ate. Meanwhile, Tova got up and wordlessly finished cleaning the counters.

"Tova, you did a wonderful job preparing *Shabbos*," said her father. Tova smiled appreciatively.

"Should I bring up some food for Imma?" asked Tova.

"No. She's sleeping now. She's not feeling so well. This round was a bit hard on her."

"I forgot to set the crock pot," said Tova quickly. She walked over to the counter and adjusted the dial.

"Tova, do you want to tell me why you got so upset before?" asked Mr. Feder.

Tova hesitated. "Motty was supposed to get the soda when he did the shopping today, and he forgot!" she exploded.

"That's what made you so upset? That there wouldn't be any soda?"

"Yes!" said Tova defensively. "That's right."

"Well, okay. Anyway, I have a few things of my own to take care of before *Shabbos*, so I'll be going upstairs."

That night, Mrs. Feder came downstairs and rested on the couch during the *seudah*. She was able to drink just a sip of grape juice and eat a bare *kezayis* of bread. By the time the soup came around, she was fast asleep.

At the end of the *seudah*, Mr. Feder woke his wife and helped her upstairs. Through the long night, Shevy heard her father help her mother to the bathroom several times. Gritting her teeth in determination, she used her mother's suggestion of thinking about all the things she had to be thankful for. For once, she was able to squelch any distracting thoughts. In a state of utter exhaustion, she finally fell asleep.

Motzei Shabbos came. After putting away the *besamim*, wine cup and *Havdalah* candle, Mr. Feder turned to Tova, who had just started washing the dishes from *Shabbos*. The two of them were alone in the kitchen, and Tova worked silently.

"Tova, I'd like to talk to you about Imma."

"Please, Abba, not tonight."

"That's just the point, Tova. Not tonight and not any other night or day."

Tova turned from her dishes and gave her father a quizzical look.

"What I mean is, you seem to be avoiding the whole issue of Imma's illness. Instead of talking or thinking about it, you get upset over soda or things like that. Do you know what I mean?"

"I don't *want* to talk about it or think about it. Why should I have to?"

"Because if you try to totally ignore it, your feelings just come out in different ways," he said softly.

"You want me to be like Shevy?" asked Tova, her voice rising and her face reddening. "She can't seem to say one word without talking about how sick Imma is. I can't stand it! Yakkity-yak, yakkity-yak, all day long! And if she's not talking about it, she's crying over it. Ugh!"

"Look, Tova, that's Shevy's way of dealing with it," responded her father. "She talks about it a lot. I'm not saying that's the only way to handle it. But it's Shevy's way, and it works for her. Now, let's talk about how you deal with it."

"I don't want to deal with it. I just want to feel normal. When I go to school, everyone has such ordinary, boring, plain lives. They don't have mothers who are going to the hospital every month. That's all I want—an ordinary, boring, plain life. I love going to school every day. It makes me feel normal. I don't have to talk about my feelings all day long!"

Mr. Feder thought for awhile. "Tova, it's good that

you're trying to make your life as normal as possible. It shows that you can cope with anything and that you're as strong as a rock! Those are wonderful *midos*, and I'm proud of you."

"Good. Could we please talk about something else then?"

"No, we can't. Because I still think you need some way of expressing yourself. It's not healthy for you to keep your feelings all bottled up inside like this. It's too heavy a burden. I don't mean that you have to talk non-stop about it, but something has to change."

"Please, Abba, I'm fine." Tova's eyes began to fill with tears. She angrily wiped them away and turned back to the dishes.

"Tova, I've thought about this for a while. You have two choices. You can either see a professional about this . . ."

"A professional?" asked Tova, horrified. "You mean like a social worker or a shrink?"

"Something like that. I'm sure Rabbi Stern can suggest some competent, *shomer Shabbos* people. It's nothing to worry about. It's something a lot of people do."

"Well, I don't want to do it!" Tova said stubbornly. She slapped down the dish she was washing, nearly breaking it, and turned around to face her father.

"Well, the second choice is easier. It's for you to write down some thoughts every day in a notebook. It would be for your eyes only, but you'd have to do it every day."

"Fine. If those are my choices, I'll choose the notebook thing."

"Good."

"Are we finished?" asked Tova bitterly.

"Sure," said Mr. Feder with a smile.

The next day after school, Tova came home and found a gift-wrapped package on her dresser. Inside was a diary, complete with lock and key. The cover contained an inscription.

To Tova, my strong, dependable, lovable daughter. Abba.

14

"Maybe it's time to call the police. We've done everything that could possibly be done," said Mrs. Feder, sitting at the table and nervously running her hand along the edge.

"I guess you're right," agreed her husband. He reached for the phone and quickly dialed the emergency number. Removing his glasses, he raked his fingers through his hair.

That Monday morning had started out as most others. Then Rabbi Alpert had called to say that although his friends had seen Motty get off the school bus, he had not shown up for class. Was Motty home, he wanted to know, or did the Feders know where he was?

A search of the school building was quickly conducted, but Motty was not found. The hours passed by without a clue of Motty's whereabouts. Mr. Feder had left work and cruised around the neighborhood, while his wife called the homes of Motty's friends. Neither of them found any sign of Motty. As a last resort, they called the police.

While they waited for the police to arrive, Yehudah came home. Mrs. Feder quickly filled him in on what was going on. Yehudah seemed quite excited by the events.

When the bell rang, Yehudah ran to get the door. He watched with interest as an officer came in and spoke to his parents.

The policeman was tall and thin. His bright curly red hair framed a wide freckled face. Yehudah sat near his mother as the officer took down information.

"Well, okay. All I'll be needing now is a recent photo of your son," he concluded.

"Yehudah," said Mrs. Feder. "Go downstairs and bring up the red photo album."

Yehudah did as he was told.

"What usually happens in cases like this?" asked Mrs. Feder.

"Well, ma'am, as you might know, in the past we've never gotten involved in a missing persons case until the person was gone for at least twenty-four hours. But nowadays, with crime levels so high and all, we respond right away, especially when the missing person is a minor.

"But the truth is, here in this town, it's a kinda quiet place, you see. Kids do run away every now and then. They always come back sooner or later, their tails tucked between their legs, if you know what I mean," he added brightly.

"Always?" asked Mrs. Feder skeptically.

"Well, almost always," he conceded.

She did not look reassured, but she handed the officer

a photo from the album that Yehudah had brought. The Feders walked the officer to the door and thanked him. Upon leaving, he almost bumped into a startled Shevy.

The Feders quickly brought Shevy up to date. "What are we going to do, Imma?" asked Shevy when they had finished.

Mrs. Feder looked at her husband, who resignedly shrugged his shoulders.

"We've done everything we can. Now we have to wait," said Mr. Feder.

"I think I'll take another drive around," he added. "Who knows? Maybe I'll find something."

He started to pick up his keys from the dining room table, when suddenly he stopped short. Someone was opening the front door.

"Hi, everyone!" called Motty cheerily as he walked into the living room. "Boy, Abba, you're home early!"

No one said a word. Mr. Feder looked at his wife in amazement. Shevy and Yehudah waited quietly to see what would happen.

Motty looked around the room and suddenly realized that something was up.

"Umm, what's the matter? Is everything okay? Imma, are you alright?" Motty's face wore a puzzled look.

"I'm fine, Motty," whispered Mrs. Feder.

"Oh." Motty's face reddened and he licked his lips nervously.

Shevy looked at her father. He was gripping his keys very tightly, his eyes narrowing. He was obviously seething with anger and trying to control himself. Finally, he spoke.

"Motty, just where were you today?"

"I, umm . . . well . . ."

Yehudah couldn't contain himself any longer and spoke excitedly. "Yeah, Motty, where were you? Imma and Abba were all upset. Abba came home early and Rabbi Alpert called from your school. A policeman came and took your picture and . . ."

"Yehudah!" Mrs. Feder sharply interjected. "Go upstairs, do your homework and don't come down until you're called."

"But . . ."

"Now! Shevy, you too."

Yehudah and Shevy did as they were told.

Mr. Feder sat beside his wife on the couch while Motty nervously stood in place.

"Alright, Motty," began Mr. Feder, his voice deliberately low and controlled. "Tell us what you did when you got off the bus."

"Well, there's a garage behind the school, and I stayed there during the day."

"Why?" asked Imma.

Motty took a deep breath. "I failed the English test, and Rabbi Alpert had told me that if I failed one more test, he'd suspend me. And . . ."

"And what?" asked Mr. Feder pointedly.

"And nothing."

"Do you know how frightened everyone was? Didn't you even think?"

"I'm sorry."

"Sorry? You've been saying you were sorry since the beginning of this school year!" exploded Mr. Feder.

"You've changed from an 'A' student and a reliable person into someone entirely different. You passed the entire first quarter of sixth grade by the skin of your teeth. You don't do your homework. You make trouble at school. And at night, you're hardly ever home!"

Motty stood quietly, shifting from one foot to the other.

"Tell me what we're supposed to do about you! We've talked to you a hundred times, but nothing seems to penetrate!"

Motty shrugged his shoulders but said nothing.

"Don't you have anything to say?" asked his father.

"No."

"Fine!" said Mr. Feder explosively. "I do! It seems that talking and screaming get us nowhere with you. Maybe punishing you will. Starting today, you are to come home immediately from school. You will go straight to your room and do your homework, and except for supper, you will not come out for the entire night. After two weeks, if your grades and behavior improve, you will be allowed to return to your normal schedule."

Motty looked up, his eyes blazing defiantly, but he still said nothing.

"Do you understand?" asked Mr. Feder.

"Yes, and I really don't care!" Motty blurted out furiously.

"What is that supposed to mean?" asked his father.

"Nothing, just nothing."

"Fine. Now get upstairs and . . ."

"Chaim, wait," Mrs. Feder whispered. "Motty, sit down and tell us what's on your mind."

Mr. Feder threw up his hands in resignation, and Motty just stood there.

"Sit down, Motty. We're waiting to hear what you have to say," his mother repeated.

Motty sat down but said nothing.

"Motty, you have about thirty seconds before I lose my patience again," said Mr. Feder.

"I don't care," said Motty, looking straight at his father.

"What does that mean?" asked Mrs. Feder.

"It means that it just doesn't matter. It means that I don't matter to you! That's what it means."

Mr. and Mrs. Feder sat in shocked silence.

"It's true! Everyone else here is treated like . . . like someone special. No one can say anything upsetting to Tova anymore, because maybe she'll explode. You can't say the word sick or cancer, because she 'just can't talk about it.'" Motty mimicked Tova's high-pitched voice.

"With Shevy, you have to go out of your way to be extra nice to her because she's so-o-o sensitive. Maybe the poor thing will cry! Isn't that terrible? And with Yehudah, well, he's just a baby. He clings to Imma all day long. We can't let him get upset. He's just too little to cope with anything at all." Motty's voice was bitter.

"But then there's good old Motty. He's not 'too' anything! Everyone else can say anything they want to him. He doesn't do his homework? Yell at him! He leaves the room a mess? Scream at him! Who cares what happens to Motty? Nobody! Who cares if it's fair or not? Nobody, that's who!

"And now you yell at me for telling the truth, but I

don't care! Go ahead, Abba, lock me up in my room for the rest of the year! I just don't care!" Motty sat there, his eyes glaring and his hands tightly clenched on the arm-rests of his chair.

Mr. and Mrs. Feder sat quietly for awhile, letting Motty calm down. Finally, struggling to control his emotions, Mr. Feder spoke.

"Motty, being fair does not mean giving the same thing to each person. Being fair means doing what is best for each individual. There's a saying, *Chanoch lanaar al pi darko.*

"I'm sorry that you've felt so abused and angry," he said. "Nonetheless, the punishment remains. In addition, I will continue to expect improvement in all areas from you. Never forget that we love you very much. Very much. Just as much as the rest of our children. I don't imagine that you believe that now, or that you even want to believe it. But maybe, one day soon, you will."

Motty stared straight ahead, not saying a word.

"You may go upstairs now, Motty. And when you get there, please give Rabbi Alpert a call. He's very worried and is waiting to hear what happened."

Without a backward glance, Motty walked slowly up the steps.

"Come in, Motty. Take your usual seat," said Rabbi Alpert wryly.

Motty sat down.

"Now listen here. You scared me very much yesterday. What you did was thoughtless and irresponsible."

"I'm sorry," whispered Motty.

"So you told me last night. You know, I also spoke to your father for quite a while. He didn't seem like he was too thrilled either. Motty, what did I tell you would happen if you caused trouble or failed a test once more?"

"I'd be suspended." Motty swallowed hard.

"Exactly. It seems that yesterday you hit the jackpot. You did both in one day.

"But there's more, of course. There's still that awful smell," Rabbi Alpert stared at Motty in silence. Motty averted his eyes but finally, with a sigh, began to speak.

"Well, about the smell . . ."

Rabbi Alpert lifted his hand and waved Motty silent. "Wait. Don't speak. Just listen." The principal cleared his throat. "Motty, you are in deep trouble. The teachers are fed up with you and your parents are upset. I'm almost at the end of my rope and there's still that awful, disgusting smell, if you know what I mean."

"I know," agreed Motty miserably.

"But prior to this year, you've always been an excellent student. Top of the class. Both in grades and in *Midos*. And I know, that somewhere deep inside of you, you want to be good again. So, I am giving you one last chance. The absolute very last one, and here are the conditions.

"As you know, the school is downstairs at a *Rosh Chodesh* assembly. The classrooms are totally empty. I will close the door to this office and give you fifteen minutes to get rid of the odor. Will that be sufficient time?"

Motty hesitated.

"Really, Motty, let's not play games."

"Yes, that will be enough time."

"Good. But that's not all. There's more. Your grades will improve, starting with the very next test. Agreed?"

"Yes."

"You will be on your absolute best behavior in class. No talking, no passing notes, no climbing trees, setting off fireworks—no trouble at all. Don't even look the wrong way."

"Yes."

"And your seat will be changed. You will not be sitting next to Eli but rather, in the front of the classroom. I will take care of that myself.

"In return for this exemplary behavior, you will be treated by myself and the teachers as if this was your first day of school. We will treat you as we would any other student. I trust that you'll make the most of it. Do you understand absolutely everything and agree to it?"

"Yes."

"Terrific, *Hatzlacha*, Motty. Now send Eli in to me. He's sitting outside the office. I think I'll have a word with him while you're deodorizing the building."

Motty began to leave and Rabbi Alpert turned his attention to some papers on his desk. As Motty touched the doorknob, he turned back around.

"Um, Rabbi Alpert. Thank you."

"Motty, you're very welcome."

15

"Let's go already! Scene five players, get up on stage! Hurry! Lunch is over in ten minutes. The play is in three days! Three! Let's get serious!" Frantically, Mrs. Levy yelled directions.

The actresses of scene five quickly assembled themselves on stage. Rivkah and Shevy sat in the audience, eating lunch while waiting for their turn.

"So, anyway," said Shevy, munching on her sandwich, "Motty is still pretty angry. Mostly at my father. But Abba is just ignoring it. Imma feels bad, I can tell, but she's taking Abba's side, as usual."

"Is he doing better in school?" asked Rivkah, opening a sandwich cookie to get at the cream.

"Well, it's only been a week, but as far as I know, there haven't been any calls from school. He got good marks on some quizzes. But boy! He used to get straight A's. I mean straight! All the time."

"I should be so lucky!"

"Well, I sure don't envy him now, Rivkah. He almost got suspended from school. The principal was really angry with him, too. I don't think my parents even know about that."

"Poor kid."

"You're not kidding. He's also stuck in his room every day after school. He still has another week to go. To keep him company, I've played Monopoly with him five nights in a row. We're both getting sick of it!"

Shevy chewed thoughtfully on the last of her sandwich. "Well, at least my mother is feeling better. It was scary when she came home last time. She was so sick."

"I remember."

"That's it!" called out Mrs. Levy. "There's no time for the next scene. Back to class. Don't forget, after school there's practice for dance and for scenes one through four."

Still talking, Shevy and Rivkah walked together to class.

"Ten points for Team A and nine for Team B!" said Mrs. Lipsett. "Next question for Team B."

Mrs. Lipsett had thought it would be a great idea to review for the upcoming science test with a contest. As could be expected, Shayna Leeba and Dinah were on opposite teams. So far, the competition had been both equal and fierce. The entire class was completely caught up in the excitement.

Soon, there were five minutes left until the end of class. Dinah's team had forty-four points and Shayna Leeba's, forty-five.

"Okay, this is the last question, worth three points," said the teacher dramatically. "Whoever answers correctly will be the winner!"

She presented the question. She looked over at Shayna Leeba's side of the room. "Okay, Team B?"

The room was silent. No one seemed to know the answer. The girls on Team B all looked to Shayna Leeba, but to no avail. After a minute of silence, Mrs. Lipsett turned to Dinah's side of the room.

"Okay, Team A, if you get the answer right, you win."

Shevy looked at Dinah. Why doesn't Dinah give the answer, she wondered? She definitely knows it—I asked her that exact question right before class, and she knew the answer but didn't get a chance to finish telling me. And Shayna Leeba was standing right next to us, so she knows Dinah knows.

The seconds ticked by. Answer it, Dinah, thought Shevy! But there was only silence.

Shevy's eyes met Shayna Leeba's. Shayna Leeba gave Shevy a questioning look, which Shevy returned.

"And . . . time is up!" said the teacher. "Team B, you're the winner."

A cheer went up from everyone on Team B.

Everyone that is, except for Shayna Leeba.

"Why did Dinah do that?" hissed Shayna Leeba, stomping over to Shevy's desk after class.

"Do what?" asked Shevy.

"She knew the answer, so why didn't she say it? I don't need her favors! You think I could care less if I won or lost? Just what is she trying to prove?"

"Shayna Leeba, when she's mean to you, you couldn't

care less! Now that she was nice, you're steaming! Why?"

"I don't know, it just bugs me."

"Shhh . . . she'll hear you. Shayna Leeba, just think about what a sacrifice Dinah made for you! Winning is very important to her, so she thinks it's just as important to you. Get it?"

"Oh." Shayna Leeba was quiet a moment, letting the idea sink in. "Yeah. I guess I see what you mean."

Shevy looked around the classroom. "Well, Dinah's still sitting at her desk, and almost everyone else is gone. It's up to you to say something to her."

Shevy collected her books, and left with a smile and a wave.

Shayna Leeba forced herself to walk over to Dinah's desk. "Umm . . . Dinah?" she began tentatively.

Dinah turned and her face reddened. "Oh, hi."

"That was, uh, what you did was really nice. I know that you knew the answer, and you let me win anyway. Thanks."

Dinah smiled and her face brightened. "You're welcome. I didn't mind at all."

There was an uncomfortable silence.

"Dinah, do you want to be my partner for the *Chumash* project?" asked Shayna Leeba. "I'd really like that."

"Really? Well, that would be great. Which topic should we choose?"

Together, the two girls considered the possibilities and decided to continue working at Dinah's house that evening.

"Unbelievable! Now I've seen everything," Ahuvah

gushed to several of her classmates the next morning.

"You're telling me!" exclaimed Sarah. "Imagine that! Dinah and Shayna Leeba working on a *Chumash* project together!"

The whole class was talking about it. It was hard to believe, but the facts were undeniable. Only Shevy, among all her classmates, wore a calm, knowing smile.

"What do you know that we don't?" whispered Rivkah.

Shevy laughed. "Nothing! Really, Rivkah, it was just a matter of two people going the extra step."

"You know, Shevy, you're talking more and more like an adult and less like an eighth grader every day. It's scary."

"Is that a compliment?"

"I don't know!"

The class quieted as Dinah and Shayna Leeba walked in together. They were deep in friendly conversation, oblivious to the others.

That night at supper in the Feder home, Yehudah was particularly talkative. "Also, we had an assembly, and a fireman told us what to do if there was a fire. I got an *alef* on my homework today! At lunch, Yitzi Shapiro gave me five cookies for my apple. We also got the school newspaper today."

Yehudah paused just long enough to take a crumpled piece of paper from his pocket. His parents smiled at each other.

"See? It's the *Tiferes Eliyahu Gazette*. Guess what? Tonight is the basketball game! Our school is playing against the Noam Yeshivah, but you're only allowed to go if you're in third grade or older." Yehudah frowned momentarily.

"Hey, Motty, aren't you going? It's supposed to be the best!"

Motty grabbed the paper from Yehudah's hand and crumpled it up. "Give me that! And stop talking already!"

"But . . ." began Yehudah.

Mr. Feder spoke firmly. "Yehudah, quiet down and finish your supper, please."

Yehudah shrugged his shoulders and picked up his spoon.

The Feder parents exchanged a knowing glance. They both knew that tonight's basketball game between Motty's *yeshivah* and its archrival would be well attended. Most of the school looked forward to it. But Motty would not be attending. It would still be a few more days until he would be allowed out of the house in the evening.

Mrs. Feder was about to speak, but her husband shook his head.

His supper finished, Motty got out of his seat and wordlessly left the kitchen. He clomped up the steps and into his room, banging the door behind him. Lying on his bed, he thought about that night's game. Not only would I have gone, he thought bitterly, but I might have even played in the game!

Motty had been doing a lot better in school these past several days, and his father continually complimented him for it. But there were still three more days of punishment to go, and to Motty they seemed an eternity.

I really hate this, he thought. I'm being treated like a baby. Baby, baby, baby! Maybe Abba'll come up here and let me go. But I won't go! Then he'll feel bad for what he did to me!

His train of thought was interrupted by a knock at the door. Well, thought Motty, maybe I will go after all!

"Come in!" he called out.

"Hi, Motty," said his mother. "May I come in?"

"Imma! I thought . . . never mind."

She sat down on the edge of Motty's bed. "Motty, I'm sorry you can't go."

"Who cares?"

Mrs. Feder gave a half smile and tousled Motty's hair.

"It's only 'cuz of Abba," said Motty bitterly.

"Well, you really caused it, Motty. You can't blame Abba. But I'm not going to talk about that. I'm sure you feel badly enough yourself. Besides, Abba and I are both pleased with how much better you've been doing in school lately."

Motty shrugged his shoulders.

"Also, Abba told me to ask you if you wanted to learn with him. He figures that you might want to skip it tonight."

"Good!"

Mrs. Feder sat silently for a little while and then left.

Ten minutes later, there was another knock at Motty's door. It was Shevy.

"Hi," said Motty.

"I'm sorry Abba's being so tough. Tova, Yehudah and I have been trying to get him to let you go for the past twenty minutes."

"You have?"

"Yup! Except that he still says no. You know Abba.

Once he says no, that's it. He did say that he felt bad and that he really wished you could go."

"If he really wanted me to go, then he could have let me!"

"Yeah, well, you know."

"Well, thanks for trying anyway," said Motty.

"Motty, I'm sorry about the newspaper," said Yehudah, suddenly walking in.

"You know, Yehudah, sometimes you talk too much."

"I know. I know. But I'm sorry, okay?"

"Yeah, yeah, it's okay."

"Good. Can I borrow your compass?" said Yehudah with a mischievous look.

Motty let out a loud whoop, grabbed Yehudah, tackled him on the bed and tickled him till he begged for mercy.

Later that evening, Shevy was searching for her misplaced calendar. She looked almost everywhere but still could not locate it. In desperation, she looked under Tova's bed.   There it is, she thought. Crawling under as far as she could and stretching out her hand, she grabbed something and dragged it towards her.

Her face fell when she saw it in the light. It wasn't her calendar at all. It seemed to be a diary. But whose diary? Tova's?

Tova never told me about this, Shevy thought. But then again, Tova was a very private person.

Should I open it, she wondered? No! Of course not! It is surely wrong to look at her private stuff.

But what if it wasn't Tova's but belonged to someone

else who left it here and was now missing it, Shevy rationalized. Well, I'll just open the front cover and take a peek at the name.

Feeling curious but guilty, Shevy opened the unlocked diary and looked inside the cover. No name.

She opened the book and leafed through the pages. The beginning entries were short, but as the diary progressed, the entries became longer. Shevy randomly opened to a page towards the end and read:

> Imma looks well today. Came home from school and Imma was at Shop-Rite. She came home and lugged the packages. She looked okay, but she was breathing pretty hard. Exertion? Who knows? She's going to be finished soon with the chemo. Will she be in remission? Who knows?
> I helped her with the packages and she told me that . . .

Shevy slammed the book shut as she heard the door opening.

"Shevy!" screamed Tova. She ran over and pulled the book out of Shevy's hands. "How could you?!"

Shevy was mortified. She looked at Tova, who had tears coursing down her cheeks.

"Tova, I was looking for my calendar and I . . ."

"Just get out of here, Shevy, and leave me alone."

"I'm sorry, Tova. I only read a few lines. I'm really sorry."

"I don't care that you're sorry. Just get out of here and leave me alone!"

Tova sat down at her desk with her back turned to Shevy. Shevy sat at the edge of the bed, swinging her foot back and forth. Minutes passed by.

"Tova," said Shevy hesitantly, "I think it's really great that you write in a diary."

"Whatever. Leave me alone."

"No, really. It's terrific."

Tova didn't answer and Shevy waited a few minutes before speaking. "Tova, does writing help you feel better?"

"I guess so," said Tova softly, her back still towards Shevy.

"Does it make you less scared about Imma?"

"Kind of. It's good to put my thoughts on paper. It organizes everything." Tova turned to face Shevy. "You know, Shevy, just because I don't like to talk about it doesn't mean that I don't care."

Shevy nodded her head. She waited for Tova to continue, but Tova sat in silence.

"Tova, I'm really sorry about opening your diary," said Shevy once again. "Forgive me?"

"I guess so. You have your flaws, but in general you're okay for a sister." Tova smiled.

"Hey, don't get all mushy on me!"

"Don't worry, I won't. And Shevy?"

"Yes?"

"If you ever even breathe near this diary again, I'll cream you!"

"Okay, okay. Don't worry. I won't touch it!"

"Good. And by the way, look what's sitting on my desk. Your calendar."

"Okay, everybody, quiet down!" called Mrs. Levy over the din. "Scene one players, let's go, up on stage. Everyone else, off! Everyone. Take a seat. At this rate we'll be here all night. So let's go!"

The actresses scrambled to their places and the action began. There were only two days left to practice the play, and this was a dress rehearsal. There would be one more practice tomorrow afternoon, and then Wednesday would be the real thing!

The tickets were already sold out. At least three hundred women and girls would fill the auditorium, and every eighth grade girl wanted to do her best.

After play practice, Rivkah and Shevy walked home together. Shevy's costume, wrapped in plastic, was draped over her arm.

"Hey, Rivkah, look up ahead. Dinah and Shayna Leeba are heading for the bus stop together."

"Unreal! You'd think they were friends forever. Dinah's really lucky that Shayna Leeba is so nice. Everyone else is nice to Dinah now because of Shayna Leeba, you know?"

"True. But it's working out pretty well for Shayna Leeba, too. Her adversary has turned into her friend," said Shevy. "Life can be really strange, don't you think?"

"I agree. But I can't stop thinking about this play. Isn't it absolutely the best?"

"I can't wait!" said Shevy excitedly, dancing in circles right there on the street.

"Shevy, aren't you even nervous? You have the main part, and all those people are coming."

"Nope," answered Shevy with a bow. "I'm not! I love every minute of it. It's fun. Yesterday, Tante Elly called and said she could make it. My mother is coming, of

course, Tova is coming and even Tova's friend Naadia is
coming. All of my mother's friends are coming too! I just
can't wait!"

"Me too. It's going to be beautiful. And we'll make so
much money for *tzeddakah*. Remember last year's eighth
grade play?"

"Yup. It was great. Not as great as this play, mind you,
but nice enough."

Rivkah laughed. "Nothing is as nice as this play, huh?"

"That's exactly right! How'd you know?" giggled Shevy.

"How's your mother feeling?"

"She's feeling great! She's back to her old self. She's
up and around. Oh, we made brownies together last
night. They're yummy! Wanna come over and have
some?"

"Thanks, but my mother really needs me. My aunt,
uncle and cousins are visiting, and there's a lot of cooking
to be done."

Shevy and Rivkah stopped in front of the Feder house.

"Well," said Shevy, dancing one more time around
Rivkah, "I'll see you tomorrow!"

"*Hasta manana,* you Mexican jumping bean!"

Shevy ran up the steps to her house and flung open
the door. "Howdy, everyone! I, Shevy Feder, have arrived
home!"

She quickly hung up her gown in the hall closet and
went into the kitchen. Her father was on the phone. Shevy
waved hello and took out the brownies from the cabinet.
Her father was intent on his conversation, but Shevy was
too busy with the brownies to pay any attention. Shortly,
he got off the phone.

"Hi, Abba," said Shevy happily. "Play practice was great tonight. The costume looks terrific! You did a great job!"

"That's good, Shevy," he said absently. "Listen. I have some bad news. Imma's not feeling well. She woke up this morning weak and tired. The doctors did some blood work and found out that her white count is down and that she has an infection."

Shevy was shocked. "What does that mean? Where is she? What did the doctor say?"

"Calm down, Shevy. It means that she has to go to the hospital for antibiotics."

"Why can't she take them at home?"

"Because she needs a very strong kind of antibiotic, one that must be done through an I.V. She'll be in the hospital for about a week."

"A week? A whole week? She never stays that long!"

"I know, but the antibiotics take a week to work. The good part is that she won't feel sick like she does from the chemotherapy."

"The good part?" Shevy couldn't believe it. She felt close to tears.

"Shev, I'd like to stay and talk to you, but I can't. I want to take Imma as soon as I can. Tova is upstairs packing for her. I'd like you to get some food ready for her."

"But . . ."

"I'm sorry, Shevy. I have no more time to talk. Please hurry with the food."

Shevy ran into the living room. Her mother was sitting on the couch, tears sliding down her cheeks.

"Oh, Imma!" said Shevy.

"Shevy, don't worry," said her mother in a forced calm tone.

Shevy put her arms around her mother. "Are you okay?" asked Shevy.

"I'll be alright. I'm just sorry that I won't make it to the play."

Shevy sat back as if struck. "Oh!"

"I won't be discharged from the hospital in time. I'm so sorry."

Shevy managed to fight back her tears and put on a smile. She wanted to talk about how disappointed she was but didn't want to upset her mother.

"That's okay, Imma," she heard herself say. "I mean, I'll miss having you there, but it's alright. I just want you to get well."

Shevy's mother gave her a hug.

"Oh! I'd better go prepare the food," said Shevy, leaping up and running into the kitchen.

Shevy muttered the first *pasuk* of her usual *perek* of *Tehillim* several times and pushed any upsetting thoughts out of her mind. She whirled around the kitchen and tried to concentrate exclusively on getting her mother's food ready. She wrapped food in aluminum foil and sealed it in plastic bags.

The doorbell rang in the front hallway.

"I'll get it!" called Shevy. She opened the door to find Tante Elly.

"Your father asked me to come over and stay with you until tomorrow morning," she said.

"Sure. Come in."

Shortly, Shevy's parents were ready to go. Her father

quickly explained that he would be staying in the hospital overnight. For the next week, he would go to work for most of the day and visit their mother every night. Tante Elly would be leaving tomorrow morning, and Shevy, Tova, Motty and Yehudah would take over the upkeep of the household.

"Well," said Tante Elly as the door clicked behind them, "anyone feel like playing Monopoly?"

Motty and Yehudah quickly agreed and sat down at the dining room table with their aunt. Tova went upstairs to her room, and Shevy went into the kitchen to call Rivkah.

"Oh, no!" were Rivkah's words upon hearing Shevy's news. "Come over to my house, and we'll talk."

Shevy ran the blocks to the Akerman house, and Rivkah quickly let her in.

"Come on in. Everyone is upstairs. I'm in the kitchen making a *kugel*." Shevy followed Rivkah into the kitchen.

"Okay. Now start at the beginning and tell me the whole thing."

Shevy tried to speak but instead burst into tears. Rivkah quickly got her a drink of water. It was several minutes before Shevy was able to compose herself enough to speak. She gave Rivkah a detailed account.

"That's terrible!" said Rivkah sympathetically.

"I know," agreed Shevy.

"Maybe she'll get better and be able to come to the play!" suggested Rivkah.

"No, Rivkah. She's got to be there for a full week. And I feel so guilty about feeling bad for myself when Imma is sick."

"Shevy, you've been excited about this play practically since you were born!"

"Yeah, I know. So was Imma. She talked about it all the time."

"So what are you going to do?"

"Nothing. There is nothing to do. But I'm not going to get all crazy about it this time, Rivkah. It doesn't help at all."

"I guess so. But don't worry, Shev. We'll all be there for you. You'll be great on Wednesday!"

Shevy attempted a smile. She stayed at Rivkah's for a little while, then glanced at her watch.

"Oh! I'd better get back. My aunt will worry." Rivkah put on her coat and walked Shevy home.

"I guess I'll ask Tante Elly to take a lot of pictures so I can show them to my mother," said Shevy.

"Pictures," repeated Rivkah, seemingly lost in thought. "Hmmm . . ." She waved good-bye to Shevy and headed home.

Shevy entered her house and hung her coat up in the hallway. Tante Elly came to greet her.

"Hi, honey. How are you?"

"Okay, Tante Elly. Did you win?"

"Of course. Have you ever known me to lose a game of Monopoly?"

"We-e-ll, remember the time, umm, I think it was last *Chanukah*, when we were all at your house and . . ."

"Please!" said Tante Elly, covering her face in mock anguish. "Don't remind me! I went bankrupt! On to more pleasant topics. Would you like something to eat, or would you like to talk awhile?"

"Umm . . . I think I'll just take a drink. Thanks."

"Well, I'll join you. I'm kind of thirsty myself."

Shevy found Tova talking on the phone in the kitchen. When Tova looked up and saw Shevy, she quickly moved into the dining room and continued the conversation in hushed tones.

Shevy turned to Tante Elly. "What do you suppose she's whispering about?"

Tante Elly shrugged her shoulders. "Who knows?"

Shevy finished her drink, said good night to her aunt and left the kitchen. Curious, she purposely walked through the dining room. Tova, with her back turned, was leaning over the phone, whispering intently.

Shevy went upstairs and got ready for bed. She lay back on her pillow, and in the quiet darkness of the bedroom she was able to think things through.

Yes, she thought to herself, I am upset that Imma won't be coming to the play, but I'll try not to fall apart this time. Yes, I am scared that Imma is sick, but I know that it is only an infection and that soon she'll be home and feeling better. With the help of Hashem, she will soon be well!

Shevy smiled even as her eyes filled with tears. She closed her eyes, repeated her now familiar *perek* of *Tehillim* and fell asleep.

The next morning, when Shevy arrived at school, she found Rivkah, Ahuvah, Shayna Leeba and Dinah huddled around their desks, talking. Shevy quietly walked over, but as she approached, Ahuvah looked up, a startled expression on her face.

"Oh! Shevy! Good morning!"

"What's going on, Ahuvah? Why do you sound so weird?"

"Weird? Who, me? Nothing is going on," insisted Ahuvah innocently.

"Come on, Ahuvah. Spit it out! You could never keep a secret and you know it," replied Shevy.

"Well . . ." began Ahuvah, red-faced.

Suddenly, Shayna Leeba punched her arm. "It's nothing!" she said stridently. "We're only talking about the play and . . ."

"And," continued Rivkah, "we're trying to decide who is the most nervous. I'm not really nervous. I think I'll do okay."

"Right," said Shayna Leeba, encouraged by Rivkah's quick retort. "I am nervous. But I have a small part, so I guess I'll be okay."

"Hmmm," said Shevy, still suspicious. "You guys are sure acting weird today. But if you want to know, I'm not nervous about my part at all. And I don't believe for one minute that that's what you guys were talking about."

"Well!" said Ahuvah, ignoring Shevy's last remark. "Let's talk about *perek beis*, 'cuz I didn't do much homework last night. I was too excited about the play, and I was practicing my part as a strict teacher. But I think Mrs. Krigsman is even stricter than I am, and she won't be too happy when I don't know the work today! Okay, guys, who's gonna help me? You or you?" Ahuvah pointed to Shayna Leeba and Dinah, who looked at one another and laughed.

Ahuvah and Dinah quickly engrossed themselves in reviewing *pesukim*, and Shevy went to her desk on the other side of the room to put her books away. All over the classroom, girls were busy talking about the play. Nervous excitement was brewing everywhere.

Rivkah turned to Shevy. "How was the rest of last night? Did you sleep okay? Did you speak to your mother?"

"Well," answered Shevy, twisting her hair around her fingers, "I got to sleep okay last night, and this morning my mother called from the hospital. She sounded good, not like she usually does when she's in the hospital. Then my father got on and said that all of us kids could visit her tonight. He said that Imma is feeling very well. She just needs that I.V. He's taking us there after supper."

"It's great that you'll be able to see her."

"I guess so. Except that I'm a bit scared about going to the hospital. I don't know," said Shevy, leaning her chair back on two legs. "I feel so crazy and mixed up. I'm so excited about the play, but I'm so sad that my mother can't be there. I just feel like running home, lying on my bed, pulling up the blanket and hiding for the rest of the day!"

Rivkah looked at Shevy, knowing that there was nothing to say.

"I won't, though. I'll stick it out here."

"Well, if you need me, I'm here for you," said Rivkah.

"Yeah, I know. Thanks."

The classroom door opened and Mrs. Krigsman walked in. The girls opened their *Chumashim* and class began.

"I don't know what's with you girls today!" said Mrs. Krigsman some time later, throwing her hands in the air. "No one seems to be able to sit still! Could it possibly be," she asked in a mock tone of discovery, "because of the play tomorrow?"

Everyone laughed.

"Alright. I shall make you a deal," she continued. "It's a one time non-refundable offer. We have thirty minutes left to this period. If you girls can manage to give me your full concentration for fifteen of them, I will give you free time after that. You may talk to your heart's content about the play or whatever makes you so restless. Agreed?"

All of the girls answered in the affirmative, and Mrs. Krigsman's *Chumash* class proceeded.

After the fifteen minutes, Mrs. Krigsman turned the class over to the girls. In only moments, the once quiet classroom was as hectic as a chicken market. Noise and giggles reverberated from every corner of the room.

Amidst the din, Mrs. Krigsman motioned to Shevy to come to the front of the room. Shevy approached her teacher, who pulled a chair next to her desk and indicated that Shevy should sit. In an effort to acquire some privacy and to hear over the background noise, Mrs. Krigsman leaned close to Shevy.

"Shevy," whispered Mrs. Krigsman. "I heard that your mother is in the hospital. I'm sorry that she's not well and won't be coming to the play."

"It's okay."

"Are you alright?"

"I'm doing the best I can."

Mrs. Krigsman squeezed Shevy's hand lightly. "Good for you! I'll be at the play. I'm sure it will be great!"

16

The large hospital elevator rumbled and groaned as the Feder family made their way up to the fourth floor. Shevy looked to her left and saw an old woman lying on a stretcher, a tube coming from her nose. Shevy's skin turned to goose bumps, and there was a knot in her belly. She moved closer to her father and turned away from the woman. When the elevator doors opened, Shevy grabbed her father's sleeve.

Mr. Feder turned to Shevy and tried to smile. "Don't worry, Shev. It will be fine, and you'll be okay."

Shevy gave her father a weak smile. Together, the Feders walked down a long corridor. Shevy stayed close to her father and was careful not to look inside any of the rooms. Mr. Feder stopped at the end of the hallway.

"Okay, guys, this is Imma's room. Make sure not to open any oxygen tanks and watch that you don't get stuck with any needles," he joked.

Everyone except Shevy laughed nervously. Shevy

165

knew that her father was joking but couldn't bring herself to smile.

Mr. Feder walked into the room first, and the rest followed close behind. Shevy looked at the first bed. There was a curtain around it that was partially closed. A sleeping woman was in the bed. Next to her was a machine that made a gentle hissing sound every time her chest rose.

Mr. Feder gently pulled Shevy along. They went further into the room, and Shevy saw her mother. As Shevy had been told, she really looked fine. Just like her usual self.

"Hi, everyone," she smiled, sitting up in her bed.

In only a minute's time, everyone was busy talking. As quickly as it had come, Shevy's nervousness vanished, and she found herself enjoying the visit.

While Yehudah was making a long-winded speech about his class trip, Shevy took a quick glance at her mother's arm. She could see something that looked like a needle attached to her mother's forearm with tape. A long, thin tube came from the needle and led up to a pole, on which hung a bag of fluid that was dripping slowly. It didn't seem to bother Imma at all, Shevy thought. She moved her hand normally, and her face didn't register any pain.

Before long, the family began to leave. "Shevy," said her mother, "stay for one more second. I just want to say that I so much wanted to be there with you. I'm so sorry! It'll be good anyway. You'll see. *Hatzlachah rabbah!* I'm sure you'll be great!"

Shevy could tell that her mother's smile was more

bravado than anything else. But she smiled in return.

"Thanks, Imma. I hope so! I'll be thinking of you." She gave her mother a kiss and then hurried to the door to catch up with the rest of the family.

The Feder children's moods upon leaving the hospital were markedly improved. There was a lot of chattering and bantering, and Mr. Feder had to remind them to lower their voices.

"Hey guys, this is a hospital. There are sick people here. Shhh!"

Two *Gemaras*, two steaming cups of cocoa and a plate of cookies adorned the kitchen table. Motty and his father sat next to each other going over a tough *sugya*. Everyone else was asleep, and the house was blissfully quiet.

"That was excellent, Motty. You have a very good grasp." Mr. Feder closed his *Gemara*.

"Thanks, Abba."

"You know, Motty, I'm very proud of how well you're doing in school these days," said Mr. Feder, draining his cocoa mug. "Your marks have improved significantly over these past couple of weeks. Your behavior has also improved . . . although I did hear something about music hooked to the P.A. that no one could turn off!"

"Music in the P.A. system?" asked Motty innocently.

"Hmmm . . ." Mr. Feder just smiled. "I met Rabbi Alpert the other day at *shul*, and he told me that he's very pleased with your improvement. But you're still angry, aren't you?"

Motty just shrugged his shoulders.

"Well, listen, and I'll tell you a story. The day you were

born, when I first held you in my arms, you looked up at me, a little baby frown on your face. From that moment on, you captured a part of my heart. It's never changed, Motty, and it never will. The love that I felt for you then has only increased steadily with time."

Motty looked sullen. "It doesn't always feel that way when I'm the only one getting yelled at all the time!"

"Yelled at?"

"You know what I mean."

"You mean the only one getting punished. Look, that's what was needed at the time. If any of the other kids did similar actions, they would get punished too. It doesn't mean I love you less. Okay?"

"I guess so."

"Since Imma became sick, everyone here has been affected, each in his or her own way. The wild behavior was your way of dealing with it. But I couldn't just let it go on. We must learn to live with what Hashem has given us. I knew you could cope better, because Hashem does not give a person a burden that is too hard to bear."

He smiled at Motty and continued. "But why focus on the past? Now, you have improved a thousand percent! You're terrific!"

Mr. Feder paused. "Now don't tell anyone else that I asked, but how *did* you get that Mordechai ben David tape hooked up to the school's P.A. system?"

Motty laughed. "You see, it's like this . . ."

"Well, good morning!" called Mr. Feder. "You're certainly up early! A whole hour early. Excited about the play, by any chance?"

"Who, me?" Shevy twirled around the room and settled into a seat. "You bet!"

Mr. Feder laughed, and he and his daughter proceeded to eat a leisurely breakfast. Their conversation centered around nothing but the play.

"I better go upstairs and get my books together," said Shevy, looking at the time.

"Shevy! You're so early! There won't be anyone at school yet!"

"I know, but I just can't sit still here any more."

"Alright. But before you go, I have something for you. Imma bought it on her way to the hospital."

"On the way to the hospital? But you were rushing to get her there fast."

"I know, but Imma insisted, so we ran into a store and Imma found this as fast as she could—which still took about an hour!" said Mr. Feder, laughing at the memory. "Anyway, here it is."

Mr. Feder passed a small box to Shevy. When Shevy opened it and looked inside, she gave a yelp of delight.

"Abba! It's perfect! It's exactly perfect!"

"Yes, I know. Imma said the same thing."

Shevy fingered the necklace in her hand. It was long and ornate, designed with flowers of various muted colors. It would go perfectly with the green moire of her French gown.

Shevy tried it on for her father, who approved wholeheartedly. "*Hatzlachah rabbah*, Shevy. I'm sure you'll do great." He gave Shevy a warm hug.

"Abba, I can't help thinking of Imma being in the hospital with an I.V. when I'm having such a good time."

"Don't dwell on it. Put it out of your mind."

"I try, Abba. But sometimes I can't help it. I get scared. I try to switch channels, and a lot of the time it helps but not always. I hope I'll be okay today."

"Shevy, of course you get scared. If you never got scared, nervous, angry or sad, you wouldn't be normal."

"Well, in that case, I guess I'm very normal!"

Mr. Feder laughed. "You'll be great today, Shev. Really!"

"Thanks, Abba."

17

"Okay, girls!" called Mrs. Levy from the stage. "Ten more minutes, and then we'll go. Clean up and make sure your costumes are alright. Everyone here knows what to do. All actresses come to the left stage to have their makeup put on."

Before anyone knew it, it was time. The seventh grade class opened the doors to let in the eager audience. Mrs. Levy quickly ushered the actresses backstage, and in a low voice gave them their final pep talk.

"This is it! The play will be starting in about fifteen minutes. You all worked hard for many weeks, and I am sure that *im yirtzeh Hashem*, each and every one of you will do great! So stand up straight and tall and do the best you can."

The eighth grade girls looked at each other and smiled eagerly.

At the left side of the stage, Rivkah noticed someone walking up the darkened steps. It was Tova.

"Hi, Rivkah," she said. "Where's Shevy?"

"She was right here a minute ago. Hmmm. I really don't know. Just look around."

Tova walked around the backstage area. Suddenly, she spotted Shevy, sitting in a corner. She was hunched over, trying to choke back tears, her shoulders shaking slightly with the effort.

"Shevy," said Tova, sitting down and gently placing her hand on Shevy's shoulder.

"Tova!"

"Shev, I know you're upset about Imma, but don't worry. You'll be okay."

"Poor Imma. She's stuck there in the hospital, and all of us are here having a good time."

"Shevy, Imma's happy for you! We're all happy for you. You look gorgeous in that gown, and I know you'll do a great job. Just concentrate on the play and forget about everything else."

Tova sat silently with Shevy for a moment. Soon, Shevy wiped away her tears. "Thanks, Tova."

"I'm going to my seat now," she replied. "*Hatzlachah*, Shevy! You'll be great. Okay?"

"Okay. And Tova, thanks for being my sister."

"Oh, Shevy, you and your mush," laughed Tova, giving Shevy a brief hug.

There was a hush in the audience as the house lights went down. Mrs. Levy stepped through the curtains and announced loudly, *"Evelyn in America!"* She spoke for a few minutes about the play, and then the large curtains opened slowly to reveal the stage.

A sound of appreciation rose from the audience. The

stage looked so realistic and alive that everyone stared in awe. The first scene took place in an airport. The American Airlines sign in the background looked as authentic as one in a real airport.

Just as the audience was admiring the scenery, Shevy came on stage. As Evelyn, she had just arrived from France to begin her life as an exchange student. She looked resplendent in the green moire, and the necklace added the perfect finishing touch.

But the true marvel was Shevy herself. She brilliantly acted the part of a proper French girl in an unfamiliar country.

Before long, the curtains closed following the first scene. Rivkah ran over and gave Shevy's arm a quick squeeze. "Fantastic, Shev! You have the audience rolling in the aisles with laughter. You're great!"

The play went on, scene after scene. There was hardly a sound in the audience for the entire production, which lasted over two hours. Everyone performed their very best. The dances were simply breathtaking. The acting was flawless. Even the scenery, costumes and props were first rate.

For the finale, all the girls lined up in rows and sang a song that Dinah had written for the play. Dinah sang the solo. She had a beautiful voice, which seemed to come from the very depths of her soul and carried to the back of the room.

At last, the curtains closed, only to open once more as all the eighth graders gave a proper final bow. It seemed that the loud cheering and clapping would never end. The entire audience stood up and gave the players a well-deserved standing ovation. The girls, with smiles on their faces, bowed one more time. And then, for the last time, the curtains closed.

Instantly, nineteen girls began dancing around and hugging each other. They all ran over to Mrs. Levy and hugged her too. Mrs. Levy was laughing and congratulating all the girls on their beautiful performance.

Shevy felt a slap on her back. "You were great! You were unbelievable!" Rivkah announced, hugging her and twirling her around.

"You were terrific yourself! The dance was beautiful!"

Everyone was coming over to Shevy and congratulating her on a job well done. Slowly, the stage filled with proud mothers, sisters, relatives and friends, all praising the actresses.

Shevy saw Tova and Naadia come on stage. "Shevy, you were fantastic!" Tova said enthusiastically. "I couldn't believe that you were the same person as my sister. Your character was so real! It was incredible."

"Thanks, Tova! I couldn't have done it without you."

The happy post-production scene continued for quite a while. Once, Shevy looked behind her and saw Tova dragging Rivkah off to the side. The two of them spoke in a huddle. As a matter of fact, as Shevy looked around the room, it seemed that a lot of the girls had begun to whisper.

"Again this whispering?" began Shevy. But her question went unanswered as more and more people crowded the stage.

After a while, most of the onlookers had left. The eighth grade class remained, still talking jubilantly.

Suddenly, Mrs. Levy quieted everyone down.

"Alright, girls. As many of you know, your job is not finished. Leave your costumes and makeup on and come outside to the cars."

"Mrs. Levy, what is this about?" asked Shevy curiously.

Mrs. Levy laughed.

"Just do as I say," she said with a twinkle in her eye.

Bewildered, Shevy followed the rest of the girls out of the building. "Rivkah," she whispered, "what is going on?"

"I guess you'll have to wait and see."

"Rivkah! Tell me! Right now!"

"I absolutely will not!"

"This is the strangest thing that's ever happened!" said Shevy, puzzled yet excited. "It seems that everyone but me knows what's going on!"

Ahuvah caught up with them, and Shevy turned to Ahuvah.

"Ahuvah, you'll tell me. What's going on?"

"Oh, nothing really."

"How could it be nothing, when the entire eighth grade is getting into cars to go somewhere that only I don't know about?"

She looked around wildly. "Ahuvah, Shayna Leeba, Rivkah, would one of you please tell me what is going on?!"

To Shevy's frustration, all of them just shook their heads and smiled. Shevy had no choice but to get into Mrs. Akerman's station wagon. As she was closing the door, she saw Tova entering Mrs. Levy's car.

As the girls rode along, they talked about the play but made no mention of their destination. What was going on?

Suddenly, the car stopped. Shevy looked up and saw familiar words: Memorial Hospital. She whirled around to face Rivkah.

"Why are we stopping here? This is where my mother is!"

"That's right," said Rivkah, smiling broadly, "and now I'll tell you what the secret is. We are going to put on a second production of the play for your mother."

Shevy's mouth dropped open, and her eyes widened. "What? What are you talking about? You can't just go in and do what you want in a hospital!"

"Oh, yeah? Come along, and I'll tell you the rest."

The entire company piled out of the cars and walked towards the hospital entrance.

"Tova called me up the night your mother went into the hospital," explained Rivkah. "She thought it would really be great for her to see you perform. So instead of her coming to see you, which was impossible, we're here to do it for her!"

"The hospital agreed?" asked Shevy in disbelief.

"It wasn't easy, but your father spoke several times to the administration and explained the idea. They finally gave their permission."

"You mean my father, Tova and you knew all about this for the past two days?"

"And Ahuvah, Shayna Leeba, Dinah, Mrs. Levy. . ." Rivkah was counting on her fingers. "Well, actually, practically everyone but you!"

"Is that what all the whispering was about?"

"You got it!" Tova giggled as she joined Shevy and Rivkah. "The hospital gave us use of a room on the first floor for the next hour."

"Does Imma know?"

"Abba is probably upstairs right now, telling her about it."

Shevy felt tears sting her eyes. "You guys are wonderful! I don't know what to say."

"So don't say anything." Rivkah and Tova exchanged smiles, both proud of what they had accomplished.

The girls walked down a long hospital corridor. Visitors and staff had curious smiles on their faces as they watched them pass, resplendent in their costumes and stage makeup.

Mrs. Levy opened a large double door and ushered the girls into a room. Shevy was the last to pass through, and as she did, she stopped to talk to Mrs. Levy.

"Thanks, Mrs. Levy! This is really wonderful!"

"It's my pleasure! Let's go. Your mother will be coming down shortly, so we'd better get ready."

Moments later, Mrs. Feder entered the room, with Tova behind her pushing the I.V. pole. Shevy looked at her mother. She looked as surprised as Shevy. Tova brought two chairs, and she and her mother sat down.

Mrs. Levy adjusted the lights as best as she could, and once again, the play began. The girls performed the first three scenes and the last two scenes. Shevy, as Rivkah observed to Ahuvah later, was even more authentic and powerful than she was the first time.

After just under an hour, the play ended and once

again the girls took their bows. The audience of two clapped as loudly as they could.

Mrs. Levy made a very short speech, saying that the girls were all happy to come and share in this special performance. She announced that their time was almost up and that the hospital would soon ask them to leave.

Mrs. Feder called out. "Wait! Please. I would just like to say a few words." Quickly, the girls quieted down and she began. "What you have done here tonight was very special. The wonderful caring that you have shown is truly inspiring. Each one of you has touched my heart with your thoughtfulness. This is truly more than *bikur cholim*."

Her eyes filled with tears. "My emotions are getting the best of me. I can't adequately express my deep appreciation for this. I know that Hashem will surely bless you many times for everything you have done tonight."

She stopped suddenly, choked by tears of joy, and Mrs. Levy quickly filled the silence.

"The cars are waiting outside, girls."

The girls started leaving, each of them bidding farewell to Mrs. Feder. Mrs. Levy whispered to Shevy that she should stay and that her father would take her home.

The room was empty except for Tova, Shevy and their mother. Shevy went over to her mother and gave her a tremendous hug.

Trying to suppress her tears, Mrs. Feder tried again to speak. "That was simply wonderful! Your friends were terrific, and Shevy, you were a real dream! Your acting was absolutely perfect! Tova, you pulled off an amazing, wonderful, stupendous, superlative escapade."

"Yeah, Tova," agreed Shevy. "This was the nicest thing. Thank you again for everything!"

Tova blushed. "You're both very welcome. Abba and Rivkah also had a lot to do with it. It was really Rivkah's idea, and Abba took care of calling the hospital a hundred times until they gave in."

Mrs. Feder stood up and walked with her daughters to the elevators. Tova took care of the I.V. pole, and Shevy held her mother's hand.

Mr. Feder was waiting in the room when his wife and daughters returned. Mrs. Feder sat down on the bed. "It was absolutely fantastic! I can't believe it! It was beautiful and touching," she said to her husband.

Mr. Feder smiled. "I knew you would like it."

"I loved it! My hands are still shaking."

Shevy, Tova and their parents stayed together in the hospital room until security came and announced the end of visiting hours. Reluctantly, the girls and their father said their good-byes. Mrs. Feder was still smiling as the three of them left her room.

18

"Three thousand five hundred and thirty-five dollars, Imma. All from one play. Isn't that the best?" asked Shevy.

"That's wonderful, Shevy. Truly wonderful. The organization in Eretz Yisrael will be very happy when they receive it."

Mrs. Feder picked up her keys from the end table. "Ready? The store will be closing soon, and we need the time."

"Ready."

As Shevy was opening the front door of the house, the telephone rang. She and her mother looked at each other.

"Leave it. Whoever it is will call back later." Mrs. Feder began to lock the front door, but the ringing continued insistently.

"Oh, I guess you'd better get it. But hurry. Tell them we'll call back."

Shevy ran into the kitchen and picked up the phone. A man asked to speak with Mrs. Feder. Shevy offered to take a message and have her mother call back, but he claimed that it was urgent.

Shevy called to her mother, who reluctantly came into the kitchen and took the telephone. The call lasted a minute or so, with only an occasional word from Mrs. Feder.

Afterwards, she set the phone on its hook and sat down heavily on a kitchen chair. Her face was white, and she looked at Shevy blankly.

"Imma! What is it? What happened?"

"Shevy, that was the doctor," Mrs. Feder stopped for breath.

"What? Tell me!"

Shevy was shaking. What could the doctor have said to make her mother look so strange?

"It's good, it's good!" Imma managed to say. "I'm in remission. It means the cancer is gone for now. *Baruch Hashem*."

Shevy ran over and gave her mother a tremendous hug. "Really? Is he sure?"

Mrs. Feder nodded.

"Imma, I can hardly believe it."

"Let's call Abba. He's still at work. You'd better dial, Shevy. My hands are still shaking."

Shevy dialed and handed the phone to her mother. Mrs. Feder started speaking, but she burst into tears and handed the phone back to Shevy, who filled her father in on the news. Mr. Feder laughed with joy and told Shevy that he was coming home immediately.

Within an hour, the whole Feder family was sitting around the kitchen table, joking with each other, laughing merrily and feeling very grateful to Hashem for the wonderful news.

EPILOGUE

"I'm going down the street to return this hammer to Mr. Lipshutz. Anyone care to join me?" called out Mr. Feder from the front door.

Shevy went to the front door. "I will, Abba. I need to take a break from all this *Rosh Hashanah* cooking, and Imma said it's alright."

"Great, let's go."

Shevy put on her jacket and left with her father. There was a nip in the air, and Shevy pulled her collar as high as it would go. Children were playing on the streets. Shevy threw back her hair and walked quickly to keep up with her father.

Mr. Feder was humming as they continued walking. Both seemed caught up in their own thoughts. After returning the hammer, they retraced their steps.

"Come, Shevy, there's the park. Let's sit for awhile and enjoy the fresh air."

"Okay, Abba."

Father and daughter sat on a bench watching children playing on the swings opposite them. Back and forth they went, shrieking in delight. Over to the left sat the children's mothers, talking to one another and enjoying the brief respite.

Mr. Feder looked at Shevy. Her forehead was furrowed, and she had a faraway look in her eyes. "A penny for your thoughts, Shev."

Shevy looked up at her father. "Well, I was thinking of last year. I was thinking that everything is so normal again."

"*Baruch Hashem*. We have a lot to be thankful for."

"Yes, we do."

"You know, Shevy, we could easily get used to things being normal again. But still, every morning, I think about exactly how good everything is. I don't know if I really thought like this before Imma got sick."

"Exactly, Abba," said Shevy. "I was thinking that even though everything is back to normal, some things are different. I mean, I think I'm different."

"Uh-huh."

"You see, last year was both the worst and the best year of my life. It was so sad that Imma was sick. But on the other hand, I learned so many things about myself."

"Yes. That's true."

"I think those things helped make me a better person. At least I try to be better. If Imma had never gotten sick, I don't think that I would be who I am today. Of course," added Shevy quickly, "I wish Imma never would have been sick, but that's the way it happened. She got sick, and I've changed."

"I agree. You've become stronger and more able to open up to others."

Shevy smiled. "Thanks, Abba. But I had a lot of help. Like Rivkah. She stood by me through thick and thin. And Shayna Leeba helped me just by being Shayna Leeba. And of course, you and Imma."

Shevy pulled out a folded piece of paper from a pocket in her jacket.

"You know, Abba, last week, Tova and I talked about Imma being sick. Can you believe it? Tova? I guess she changed too."

Shevy thought for a moment before she continued. Children were laughing in the distance.

"Anyway, Abba, Tova is able to express her feelings so beautifully in writing. She's been writing in a diary for more than a year. Did you know that?"

Mr. Feder smiled but didn't say a word.

"At first," Shevy continued, "I didn't understand why she did it. But it seemed like such an interesting idea.

"She wrote a poem. It's so perfect. It really is. It really describes last year."

Shevy unfolded the paper. "Here, Abba, would you like to read it?"

Her Abba took the paper and read:

If only pain were wiped away,
And tears and sadness would not stay.
If only I could run away,
And greet with joy a bright new day.
If only I could wave my hand,
And change it all—it would be so grand.

I'd laugh and sing and cheer and play,
A nasty word I'd never say.
But, alas, alas, it's not to be,
This morning's here to stay with me.
This thing, this thing will not desist,
In endless battle it does persist.
This thing, I cannot change at all,
But deep inside, I will be tall.
It's sad, it's true, I must admit,
but I will not give in to it.
For joy and triumph come from within,
And with Hashem's help, *I* will win.
I'll laugh, I'll sing, I'll cheer, I'll play,
For only *I* can make the day.

Mr. Feder read it and then reread it. Slowly, he refolded the paper and looked at Shevy. "It is perfect, Shevy. It really is."

Father and daughter stood up and together made their way home.

GLOSSARY

ahavas Yisrael: love of Israel

baruch Hashem: thank Heaven

Bavlim: Babylonians

besamim: spices

bikur cholim: visiting the sick

boker tov: good morning

brachah: blessing

Chanukah: Festival of Lights

chassid(im): adherent(s) to *chassidus*

chassidus: Jewish pietist movement

chavrusa: study partner

cherem: excommunication

chessed: kindness

Chumash: Five Books of the Pentateuch

daven: pray

dinim: rulings

Erev Shabbos: Friday

Gemara: part of the Talmud

Hakadosh Baruch Hu: the Holy Blessed One

Hashem: G-d

hatzlacha: success

Havdalah: concluding ritual of *Shabbos*

kezayis: the size of an olive

Kislev: Jewish month

kollel: Torah study center

kugel: *Shabbos* dish

lashon hora: slander

melaveh malkah: post-Shabbos meal

menorah: candelabra

midos: character traits

mitzvah (mitzvos): Torah commandment(s)

Motzei Shabbos: night after the Shabbos
pasuk (pesukim): verse(s)
perek: chapter
Rosh Chodesh: New Month
Rosh Hashanah: New Year
seudah: feast
Shabbos: Sabbath
shamayim: Heaven
shomer Shabbos: Sabbath observer
shul: synagogue

siddurim: prayer books
siyum: conclusion
sugya: Talmudic topic
Sukkos: Festival of Tabernacles
Tehillim: Psalms
Tishah b'Av: The Ninth of the month of *Av*
tzaddekess: righteous woman
tzeddakah: charity
yashan: last year's harvest
yeshivah: Torah school

A Letter To My Friend In Russia

Hello dear Inna! I've received your letter for which I am very thankful and now I decided to write you back. In our school it is so much fun. I didn't go to public school. I went to a special school—Yeshivah. I called this school special, because the students who learn there are all Jewish and that's why you also have to learn many subjects in Hebrew. It is very, very hard, but I think I can mange it. In this school, they teach you lots of new things. Let me explain one thing to you first. You know that I am Jewish, and I know that you are Jewish. To be Jewish is not enough; you also have to be religious. The word Religion means to believe in something. Jewish religion means to believe in G-d. Of course, you will have a question right away. What is G-d? G-d is not a person, but G-d created the word; He created me and you and everybody else. I know what you are thinking, that in Russia everybody says that nature created the world, people, trees, flowers and many other things, but isn't that stupid. There is only one G-d in this world, and he is the one that created it. G-d is like a King. It is like He tells us what to do. Also, you can't see Him but remember something; He is watching everybody in this world from the Heaven no matter where you are, whether it be in Russia or America. I know that you are not going to understand what I just wrote and you will have millions of questions. I understand. You know yourself that in Russia G-d is forgotten, but did you know that before World War II the people who were Jews were religious? It is very hard to become religious. There are lots of things you have to know in order to be religious. If you and your family would get here, it would be much easier to explain it to you. It just cannot be all written in a letter; it is just impossible but I think you understood a little bit.

Love,
Anna